GEORGE W MACPHERSON has fo
handed down through generations ᴏɪ ɪɪɪs ɪaɪɪɪɪy aɪɪᴜ ɪɪaᴜ
become one of the best known traditional storytellers in
Scotland. George's storytelling technique is both memorable
and distinctive, capable of captivating any audience, young or
old, all over the world.

George has published three books with Luath Press:
Highland Myths and Legends (2001) and *Celtic Sea Stories*
(2009, new ed. 2016) and *The Old Grey Magician* (2017),
as well as contributing to many magazines and papers.
A participant in the Scottish Storytelling Festival for many
years, he also organises the annual Skye and Lochalsh
Storytelling Festival and opened the Commonwealth Heads
of State Convention in Edinburgh with one of his stories.
George lives in Glendale on the Isle of Skye.

Sgiath

Amazon Queen of Skye

GEORGE W MACPHERSON

Luath Press Limited

EDINBURGH

www.luath.co.uk

First published 2019

ISBN: 978-1-912147-93-9

The paper used in this book is recyclable. It is made from
low chlorine pulps produced in a low energy, low emission
manner from renewable forests.

Printed and bound by Bell & Bain Ltd., Glasgow

Typeset in 11 point Sabon and Libra by Lapiz

preface

WHEN I WAS THREE YEARS old, my grandfather took me on his knee and told me a story. Then I had to tell it back to him. He would say, 'No, that's not the way it was' and he would retell it until he was happy that I was telling it as he told it. From then until the age of ten, I learned stories from my grandfather, father, grand uncles and grand aunt and many other old storytellers from many areas. When I was ten, I was allowed to tell a story outside our own house for the first time and from then on, I was expected to gather and re-tell from the oral tradition, which I still continue to do.

I was intrigued by the way stories of Sgiath, the Amazon Queen appeared and that, although they were told by tellers from many parts of Scotland, they remained the same and were always credited back to Skye even if set in Argyll or other districts. Another thing I noted was that the tellers appeared to give a special reverence to those stories and even in some cases would only tell the stories if their heads were covered. Having heard and learned stories of Sgiath over the past many decades, I felt that the time was right to put them down in print lest they be lost. I also still tell them in different parts of the world and to groups visiting me here in Skye so that the original flavour of the stories can continue to the present times.

Many academics and tradition bearers have argued and discussed the name 'Sgiath' and whether the Isle of Skye is named after the Queen or whether the Queen was named after the island. Possibly the first written reference is that of Ptolemy, the cartographer of the island, in 120 AD, where he gives it as Sketis (Old Gaelic, Skeitos; modern Gaelic, Sgiath). However, in *The Annals of Ireland* in 581 AD, it is given as Sgith and later is given as Scith or Scia. This is applied to both the island and to the Queen. Her name is also spelled Scáthach or Sgathaich in Irish mythology.

Some scholars such as Martin Martin in 1695 have claimed the name Skie or Sgiath means 'winged isle'. Dean Munro also offers this derivation. Other early researchers translate it as 'cloudy' or 'shadowy'.

No definite answers have been reached and the origin and meaning of the name remains as shadowy as the character and the island itself. The connections between the two remain clear, however. Dunscaith Castle, whose Irish name Dun Scathiag is thought to have been inspired by her, was Sgiath's home on the island. Furthermore, there are mentions of her in the histories of places throughout Skye from Glendale to Tarskavaig.

I hope that this book will bring to interested parties an insight into the life of Sgiath and perhaps give impetus to some to study her times and teachings. I hope that by compiling this book using the oral tradition and checking written mentions for confirmation of dates and subjects taught, I have managed to give to scholars of Celtic tradition a guide to discovering more of a tradition which has been severely suppressed and denigrated by other civilisations yet has still survived in some form – for example, many of the saints and ritual in the Christian church. Possibly part of this suppression was due to the equality of women and the democracy of the Druids which was anathema to many later civilisations.

It is interesting to note that many of the principles for which Sgiath and her Amazons fought still resonate in the modern world in the struggle for both female empowerment and equality for all, regardless of gender, race or creed. It appears on reflection that things change yet remain the same.

Beannachd Leibh
George W Macpherson (Seoras)

acknowledgements

I WOULD LIKE TO THANK many people who have supported me in writing this book and to the many storytellers of my younger days who gave me stories of Sgiath and her teachings – sadly those tellers of some 70 to 80 years ago are now all gone. Perhaps they still tell their stories in some of the Druidic other worlds.

Special thanks should go to my wife Morag for putting up with my burying my head in research and perhaps ignoring what should have been more pressing matters.

chapter one

t was a day of days. Thunder rumbled, rolled, roared and reverberated round the rocks in the mountains. Great shards of jagged lightning seared across the sky or flashed in sheets of blinding light showing trees and bushes bending their heads beneath the force of a howling gale which drove the lashing rain horizontally before it. Animals of all types cowered in whatever shelter they could find trembling in fear. Men, women and children clung to each other in dread inside their houses, hoping against hope that they would see another day.

In the midst of all the chaos a woman strained and writhed in the agonies of birth. At the very peak of the storm, there emerged from her womb a baby girl who, even as she entered the world, complained vociferously against her fate. Those in the room were astounded by the vigour and vitality of the child except for the Old Grey Magician who, bending over the babe, said, 'This is the seed of the God of War who chose the mother of his child to be a mortal woman. This tiny babe shall become the greatest warrior Queen who ever lived. In her shall be combined the skill in arms of her father and the cunning wiles of her mother and I shall give to her the magic powers she shall need and her name will be Sgiath.'

As the Old Grey Magician put his blessing upon the child, the storm was stilled and the sun shone out so that all the people knew that a great one had been born. Yet despite the joy of the people, the Old Grey Magician was downcast in his own mind for he knew this was only a beginning. There was before him and the newborn babe a long and weary road of training, self-sacrifice, and great and terrible decisions before the babe could become the great Queen, which was her destiny.

For now, the infant would suckle at her mother's breast but, before much time had passed, she must be moved to a different way of life and a different way of thinking. The responsibility for this would be upon the Old Grey Magician and his knowledge of what lay ahead filled him with both dread and joyous anticipation.

Of all these things the baby was not aware, but she grew quickly, not only physically but also mentally, speaking, seeing and knowing in a way that was far beyond her years. Yet her infant years were full of happiness in the company of her mother and the other children, amongst whom she was raised in the commonality of upbringing which was the Celtic way. Still even in those tender years, there shone through the qualities of leadership: she came first in all the games and where she went others followed.

However happy her infancy, it was not long, for the Old Grey Magician appeared on her third birthday and said, 'Now is the time of prophecy fulfilled and the training begins.' Without further ado he led her away to start her new life and no one dared to deny or question his authority, least of all the mother of the child.

The Old Grey Magician strode across the moor with Sgiath almost running on her young short legs to keep up with him but he paid her no heed. Even when eventually she pleaded for a break just to catch her breath, he only looked at her and said, 'You can choose to keep up or die here on the moor and all our hopes die with you.'

Then Sgiath said, 'I shall keep up and fulfil all you have promised' and she kept up. Despite the pain that brought out scalding tears.

Now began seven years of ceaseless training in all forms of martial arts and magic. Several other children all older than Sgiath were also under the tuition of the Old Grey Magician but on Sgiath he concentrated all his efforts, to such an extent that she was at times almost overwhelmed.

Within days of her arrival, the Old Grey Magician took her outside and made her stand on a rabbit skin, warning her that she must not step outside the edge of the skin. Then he told the other children to hurl wads of earth and mud at her from all directions. Sgiath did her best to duck and dodge but, despite her best efforts, she was soon spattered with dirt. The Old Grey Magician then told the others to hurl stones at her and now she had to dodge in earnest to avoid the pain of being hit. This she did much better than before, yet the Old Grey Magician was not happy and told her that this would be done to her each day until not a single stone hit her, and then they would move on to other things. Within three days, not one stone hit Sgiath and the Old Grey Magician told her that she could now move on to harder training.

Hard and hard indeed was her training now for the Old Grey Magician now brought in warriors from many different lands who were the most skilled in their own type of arms, whether that was sword, spear, axe or club, bow and arrow, stave or knife. Sgiath had to become better than the best in each and every discipline. Even though she might be bruised and battered or wounded, only death or victory permitted her to stop. Because of her speed in learning and her unyielding spirit, she became master of every form of armed and unarmed combat.

But she still had to learn things of magic and knowledge taught by the Old Grey Magician until there came a day when he said, 'Knowledge now is yours but you must add to it all your life. Now is the time for your second birth and your choice of the life before you. Before your second birth, you must stay with the Wise Woman for a week so that she may teach you what you need to know of the

ways of men and women. You must go through
the rites of passage taking you from childhood
to womanhood. Then when you have become a
woman according to the rites, I shall take you
to your second birth a far greater trial and only
granted to the few selected ones and even some of
them fail the test.'

chapter two

After Sgiath's time with the Wise Woman was over, the Old Grey Magician said to her, 'Follow me now for now is the time for you to face the second birth in the womb of Mother Earth.'

Sgiath followed him and, although thoughts of terror and strife plagued her mind, she knew this was her destiny however and whatever it befell.

For mile after mile she followed the Old Grey Magician, until they reached a place unknown to Sgiath where the Old Grey Magician stopped at a small hummock of a hill. He laid his hands upon a large round flat stone in the side of the hummock and it rolled aside to reveal a black hole giving access to a dark passageway leading down into the Earth.

'Inside the hill,' said the Old Grey Magician, 'the tunnel leads to 27 steps plus two and then to a chamber deep below. Halfway down is a resting place and it is the last place you can turn back if you decide you do not want to see your fate. If you go down into the chamber, you will see your future and you will be reborn of Mother Earth. The decision is yours but you must go down naked as you were born, and without weapons or food.'

Sgiath was already sure of what she wanted and immediately stripped off her earrasaid which she had only just qualified to wear after her rites of passage. Without further ado, she stepped forward naked as she was born to the entrance ready to face whatever lay ahead.

At first, there was a dim light inside the passage from the entrance but this soon gave out and the darkness became intense. Feeling her way along, Sgiath reached the top of the stairs and boldly stepped on until she reached the resting place. She took no rest there but carried on down to the bottom of the steps where, by pacing and feeling, she found herself to be in a beehive-shaped chamber with a floor of solid rock and walls built of stone, the apex of which she could not reach. Now the darkness was so intense it felt as if it was a mass of wool wrapping around her and blotting out her senses. Settling into the chamber, she waited to see what might transpire.

The cold and the dark seeped into her very bones and she entered a state of live dreaming. In this state, she saw what lay ahead of her if she chose the right path. Sitting there with no measure of time or sense of movement, she made her choice and embraced her future.

As soon as her choice was made, she heard a roaring sound and suddenly found herself engulfed by water which picked her up and tossed her like a leaf. She struggled to keep her head above the flood but she was forced up to the coned apex of the chamber and unable to rise further. She felt the water close over her head. Just as she thought she was drowned, the water suddenly receded and she dropped on the floor of the chamber like a rag doll. When enough strength returned to let her crawl up the steps, she made her way back out to the entrance where the Old Grey Magician waited.

'Three days and nights you have been in the womb of Mother Earth,' he said, 'and glad was I to see them pass for I knew you had chosen your path and chosen the right one. So now you are of the two births and your name will be great as will your deeds. You and I must now go on our separate roads but always my magic will go with you. I give you now Gae-Bolg, a spear that never misses and kills whatever it hits. In time, you will pass it on to the one man of your heart when the time is right. But I must place on you a *Geisa*. In days to come, your sister Aoife will take up arms against you but you yourself must not kill or injure her though you could easily do it.'

Sgiath took the spear and said, 'I take the spear and with it and my staff, I will face the world and use them well and I accept the *Geisa* you lay upon me. Now I give my gift to you. That is to lie with you this night so you will be my first man, though I will know many in my life.'

'Old as I am,' said the Old Grey Magician,
'I gladly accept your gift, but the day will come when
you will meet a hero who will be your one man.'

So it was that they lay together that night and
each enjoyed the other but when Sgiath awoke
in the morning the Old Grey Magician was gone.
Sgiath put on her earrasaid, picked up her spear
and staff and walked on alone to face her life
to come.

chapter three

As Sgiath walked across the moor, the grey mist swirled around making ghostly shapes that twisted and turned in patterns that none could follow, much like the thoughts in Sgiath's mind. All she knew was that somewhere ahead lay her future if she was strong enough to take it.

After walking for some time, Sgiath heard the sounds of staffs clashing and the grunts and cries of combat. She went forward more cautiously and came to the edge of a hollow. Looking over the edge and down into the hollow, she saw a girl about her own age being attacked by three men. The girl was putting up a good fight against the men and her staff was leaving its mark on them, but the staffs of the men were also leaving their marks on the girl. Sgiath saw she would soon be overwhelmed and the men would have their way with her. Sgiath charged down into the hollow whirling her own stick and, in a very short space of time, the three men lay senseless on the ground.

'I give my gratitude to you,' said the girl. 'Without your help they would have got what they wanted. They are three brothers from my village

and the elders said I must lie with the youngest.
I would not for I wanted to pick my own first man
but now I cannot go back to my village for their
family would kill me for shaming them.'

'I picked my own first man,' said Sgiath. 'Now
I travel my own road to become a great Queen as
I have seen in my future. If you choose you can
follow me and share my dream.'

'I will gladly follow you,' said the girl. 'My
name is Enya and I, too, have a dream that I feel
may come true with you.'

So together they walked across the moor
towards the sun setting behind the blue sheened
mountains. That night they slept in a nest in the
heather with their earrasaids for warmth. Waking
at the break of day, they set off to find what
the day might bring. As they strode through the
heather, Sgiath noticed that Enya was studying her
closely but trying not to show it.

'Why are you looking at me in that way?' asked
Sgiath. 'If you want to know something just ask.'

Enya hesitated then said, 'I am wondering
how good you are with your staff. I saw you use it
yesterday but you surprised them. Perhaps you are
not as good as me.'

Sgiath laughed and said, 'That can soon be
settled. You have your staff and I have mine. Let us
fight now and see who is better.'

Without more ado, they started to fight but
Enya soon found she was no match for Sgiath.

If she attacked, Sgiath parried all her blows and either whisked her staff out of her hands or rattled her ribs until she had to concede Sgiath was indeed a master of the staff and Enya asked her to teach her so that she too could be a great exponent of the art.

'Gladly will I do that,' said Sgiath, 'for you have the bravery that I seek and the will to learn.'

Each embraced the other and they continued on their way in contented friendship.

chapter four

giath and Enya walked on together for some days and every day, they had a session of fighting with the staff. Sgiath was a great but very hard teacher, but Enya was a quick learner and was happy to work hard to learn the skills of Sgiath. Soon she had reached a stage where she could almost hold her own yet was not quite her equal.

Their wandering led them down to a small village by the sea which appeared to be occupied only by women and one or two old men.

'This is a strange thing to see – a village without children or men,' said Sgiath. 'There must be something wrong. Let us find out what it is.'

Enya agreed and together they walked into the village and asked the women the reason there were no children or men. At first, the women were reluctant to talk but being reassured that Sgiath and Enya were alone, they told their story.

'You can see we are only a small village. There were never many men here, just ten of them, but we were happy here and the men tilled the fields and hunted in the hills. They kept us fed and we cooked for them and attended to their needs but a tribe of wandering people came upon us. They killed our men and ate them and we know they will come back to kill and eat us as well, so we have hidden the children in caves in the hills. We and the old men will be eaten by them but then they will travel on and our children will be safe.'

Sgiath was horrified and enraged by their story. She asked them, 'Why do you not fight those cannibals? What have you to lose?'

'Oh,' said the women, 'we have few weapons to fight – only some clubs and one or two spears – and we have no one to lead us. If we fight them, they may find our children.'

'If they kill you, they may still find your children. But if you kill them, your children will be safe. Some of you may die but you give your life for your children, what more can you do? Enya and I will lead you if you will follow our plan and we shall win.'

So spoke Sgiath and waited for their answer.

chapter five

After some discussion, the women decided they had nothing to lose. They came to Sgiath and Enya and said, 'If the two of you lead us as you said and tell us your plan, at least we will have done the best we can.'

The two old men came to Sgiath. 'We are old and our legs can no longer climb the hill or chase the deer but we can still pull our bows and launch an arrow. We would be glad to do this to help save our grandchildren, even if we lose our own lives.'

'I accept your offer gladly,' said Sgiath. 'You shall have a place in my strategy and honour shall be yours.'

Now Sgiath set out her plan. 'When the cannibals come back to the village, they will not be expecting any opposition so we will let them come into the centre of the village. When they see the tribe coming, the women in the houses before the centre will run from their houses into the houses past the centre. The tribe will chase them but when they do, the women will all come out from their houses with their clubs and any other weapons they can get and attack the tribe. They will be led

by Enya. The old men will be hiding behind
one of the first houses and when the tribe passes
chasing the women, they will fire their arrows into
their backs and kill or injure as many as they can.
I myself will be hidden behind another house and I
will charge out after the first arrows are fired and
I shall kill many. Between us we shall kill them all!'

Sgiath set about putting the women and the
two old men into their positions. She and Enya
made sure that everyone in their group was certain
of what they were to do. By the time the women
were arranged, a look-out who had been posted by
Sgiath ran to say that the cannibal tribe were on
their way.

'Now is our hour of glory. Come and we shall
fight and win for the love of our family and the
honour of women!' cried Sgiath.

Just as Sgiath had foretold, the cannibals saw
the women running to the houses at the rear of
the village and chased after them with shouts
of glee. But their glee turned to cries of alarm
as the women led by Enya turned and attacked
them with all the fury of despair. However, the
cannibals were more skilled and better armed and
they rallied quickly. Even as they did, the two old
men launched their arrows into the backs of the
cannibals, killing three and wounding two more
and, at the same time, Sgiath charged down upon
them and hurled Gae-Bolg, killing six with her first

throw of the magic spear. As she leapt to regain Gae-Bolg, she slew two more with her staff.

Now she was confronted by the leader of the cannibals, a huge red-haired giant of a man wielding a great two-handed sword. Before Sgiath could lift Gae-Bolg, he swung the sword in a stroke that could have cut Sgiath in half but she leapt into the air over his sword. As she landed, she picked up Gae-Bolg and, in the same motion, she launched the spear and it hit the leader of the tribe. He felt the spear strike and pulled himself to his full height to make one more swing of his sword but, even as he did, the sword fell from his nerveless fingers and he crashed to the ground.

Panic sped through the cannibals as they saw their leader die and many of their tribe also lying dead and they turned to run. But now the blood lust was upon them all including Sgiath and Enya, and the killing did not stop till every cannibal lay dead.

chapter six

After the killing was over and the bloodlust had abated, Sgiath and Enya began preparations to leave. Despite the women's pleas for them to stay as leaders of the village, Sgiath said she must continue on her journey to find her destiny, and Enya said she would follow Sgiath anywhere. They were soon ready to travel on when five of the women came and asked to join Sgiath on her quest.

'We no longer want to stay here. We have tasted blood and seen our own strength and we would follow you and fight for you,' they said. 'Three of us have no children and of the other two, one's child died and the other's child is old enough to be left here and we are still young and strong.'

'If you follow me you must train to fight every day and learn the use of weapons of all kinds, even your bare hands, and you must be prepared for hardship or death,' said Sgiath. 'The choice is yours.'

The women did not hesitate. 'Our choice is already made: we go with you.'

'The magic of seven is now with us and we shall go on to great deeds, for the Gods are smiling on us and honour will be ours,' said Sgiath.

The small band of seven women set their faces to the setting sun and walked on to face whatever fate might bring.

* * *

Now their training began. Sgiath and Enya were very stern teachers, punishing mistakes severely and driving the women on to standards they never thought to see. Each of the women had to learn to use all the weapons they had seized from the cannibals as well as unarmed combat, but each one of them absorbed all the pain and doubt involved and came back for more.

There came a day when Sgiath felt the women had reached as high a standard as possible in the time she had to teach them. They had walked far and were now coming to areas where they might not be welcome and might have to put their new skills to the test.

'Today,' said Sgiath, 'each of you will pick your favourite weapon and fight either Enya or myself and you shall see how skilled you have become, but also how much you have still to learn for you must always keep learning.'

chapter seven

As Sgiath and her small band of warrior women proceeded on their way, they came to a large village which they approached with caution, as they knew they might face a hostile reception.

To their amazement and delight, they were welcomed with open arms and shown a house that they could use and be comfortable in during their stay. The villagers shared with them their food and drink and other facets of hospitality.

Sgiath and her band were happy to rest in comfort for a time and enjoy the friendly atmosphere of the men and women of the village. They learned that the Wise Woman of the village had foretold their coming and had told the people that they should welcome them as honoured guests.

On the second day of Sgiath's visit, the Wise Woman came to see her. She said to Sgiath, 'I am Mordu and I have five daughters, the oldest of whom is the child of the Old Grey Magician, who was my mentor and first love. Now I wish to give myself and four of my daughters to you. My eldest daughter will stay in the village and take my place as the Wise Woman. My younger daughters are all trained in arms as I myself was trained by the Old Grey Magician and am still fit and active. I also have much knowledge of the use of herbs in healing illness and treating wounds. If you are willing to take us into your band of women, we shall serve you well and your time as Queen shall come.'

'You will be a welcome addition to our group,' said Sgiath, 'for I too was a pupil of the Old Grey Magician and he was my first man. You and your daughters shall fight with us but all shall train like Enya and I and all members of our band.'

'I would expect nothing less,' said the Wise Woman. 'When you leave our village, we go with you to wherever it might lead us.'

Two days later, Sgiath and her band of female warriors left the friendly haven of the village and with them went the Wise Woman and her four younger daughters.

chapter eight

After leaving the village, Sgiath and her Amazons were surprised to be met by small groups of men and women who had heard of Sgiath's expedition and her deeds and wished to join in her adventure. Sgiath and Enya talked to the men and women, picking out from the women those they thought would be of value to them. All the women had to promise faithfulness and loyalty to Sgiath's cause and to agree to be trained in the arts of war and the use of arms.

Sgiath refused to allow any men to join her band and if any man questioned her judgement and challenged her, she would allow them to choose their favourite weapon, then she would fight and defeat them. Some of the men, although beaten, refused to surrender to Sgiath and then she killed them, but most survived to go back to their home and boast they had once fought Sgiath and lived.

So the word of her great skill was carried to many villages by the survivors and even more women wished to follow her. Yet she knew that the test for her small Amazon army would come soon and she hoped her belief in her women warriors would be confirmed. However, she feared that they might, despite her training, prove to be unable to overcome their own fears and prejudices in the reality of battle. But only time and actual combat could give the real answers. Sgiath showed no trace of these doubts to her warriors but tried instead to convey to them a sense of invincibility, a sense which would be tested before long and tested to the full.

chapter nine

As Sgiath and her growing band of followers moved on, they came to a wide glen with a free-flowing river in the centre of it and fine flat fields on either side of the water, with beautiful views across the sea to distant islands. They felt the warmth of the sun on their faces and bodies. It was as if they had entered paradise, but this paradise was not theirs to enjoy for long, for at the broadest part of the glen a strong host of armed men stood in battle array.

A tall, young, well-built man came forward and demanded to talk with Sgiath: 'I am Chief of this area. I have heard of you and your female warriors and how you killed the tribe of cannibals, but I tell you now you shall not cross this glen for my men and I will slaughter you and your women unless you leave this area, never to return.'

Sgiath looked at him and laughed and answered. 'Every cock crows loudest in its own midden. Neither you or your warriors frighten me or my women. Yet I will not force a battle, allow us to pass and we will not harm you. But I will not draw back from battle either. If you are as good a man as you make out, you and I could meet in single combat to settle this matter, and whichever of us wins today will become Chief of this area.'

'No indeed,' replied the young Chief. 'My men and I will kill you and your Amazon warriors to set an example to all those who would try to usurp my authority… After all, you are only women!'

'So be it,' said Sgiath. 'You have brought your fate upon your own head and that of your men.'

The Chief went back to his men and led them in a wild, disorganised charge against the Amazon warriors, expecting a quick and easy victory. Sgiath, however, had arranged her warriors in an arrowhead formation with herself at the point nearest the enemy and Enya and one of the Wise Woman's daughters on the tips of the triangle.

As the Chief's men rushed on, they were split by the triangle of female warriors, especially by Sgiath who was wielding the sword she had taken from the leader of the cannibals – a sword like no other. Its blade was fairly broad and not too long, its point sharp as a needle and its edges so sharp and strong that they could cut through the wooden and leather shields of the warriors and through the hardened leather armour as if through butter. It gleamed bluish grey in the sunlight, reflecting the sun's rays. When Sgiath had killed the Chief of the cannibals and taken his sword, he had killed three of the village women with one swing of it. Now the sword was hers and with it she wreaked death and havoc on the Chief's men, cutting off arms and legs and thrusting through shields and armour as if no protection existed. When the men drew back from Sgiath, they met the line of the other women who killed many of them. After that first mad charge, the Chief's army drew back to gather for another attack but, before they could launch it, Sgiath led the triangle of her Amazons in a charge that cut straight through the bewildered mass of men.

Their ranks broke up and they started to flee but Sgiath released her Amazons to pick their own target and she herself cut her way to where the young Chief was also fleeing the field. Realising that he could not outpace Sgiath, he turned to face her. Even then, Sgiath offered him a chance to live, telling him that if he surrendered his sword and pledged loyalty to her, he could live. He refused her terms and tried to smite her with his sword, but she parried his blow and decapitated him with one swing of her sword. His head flew into the air and landed amidst the feet of his men. Seeing this, his men threw down their weapons and surrendered.

Sgiath called back her Amazons from their slaughter and set the Wise Woman the task of tending to the wounded of both the Amazons and the dead Chief's men.

chapter ten

giath now was hailed by the survivors as the new Chieftainess of the area but she was not interested. She had much greater ideas in mind but she felt that she must do something to stabilise the village and the families there. She called a meeting of the elders and laid down her plan for the governance of the area.

First of all, she appointed the Wise Woman as the Chieftainess to guide the village in implementing and setting up new laws – laws which would apply to everyone in the area whether male or female. She said a stone of judgement must be set up at which complaints could be made and fair and honest judgement would be given by the Wise Woman and two other judges appointed by her.

To ensure confidence in laws and order, if the leader of the area died or became unable to rule then all adults in the district would vote for and elect a new leader, who would continue the laws set by the previous leader and when necessary make new laws to make sure that everyone had equal rights. If the leader proved to be incompetent or a bad ruler, they could be deposed and a new leader elected. The leader would also ensure that all the children in the area, both male and female, would be trained in art, science and war.

Having set out her plan, Sgiath and her now considerable band of Amazon warriors continued on their way, leaving the Wise Woman and three of the most trustworthy Amazons behind to ensure her plans were implemented.

chapter eleven

giath and the rest of her warriors headed west to follow where fate would lead them and all the time they trained in skills of arms. Even more woman came to join them, so their numbers swelled until they became a strong and disciplined army with the confidence to face any foe.

It was as well that they were ready for word of them had spread and they received a hostile reception at many of the places their journey took them through. Yet always Sgiath gave peaceable options and only fought if forced to do so. The areas where they had to fight were conquered by the Amazons and in each place Sgiath set a form of government modelled on their first conquest and she appointed a Chieftainess with a bodyguard of three trustworthy Amazon warriors in each area. But she herself marched on with her small army for she had seen her future and was determined to fulfil it.

Now some of the Kings of larger and smaller kingdoms had heard of the deeds of Sgiath and of her Amazons and they were alarmed, especially so the smaller kingdoms. Three of the Kings of smaller kingdoms met and decided to combine their forces to march to meet Sgiath and overwhelm her by outnumbering her small army. They also still had some contempt for the idea of an army of female warriors, for after all women were soft and fearful creatures, made to serve men and have babies.

Soon the Amazon scouts that Sgiath sent out ahead of her army reported that a very large force of warriors were gathered on the side of a mountain at a place Sgiath's army must pass through. Sgiath studied the information and worked out a plan, which she told to her Amazons and then they moved onwards to meet the army of the Kings.

Sgiath formed two thirds of her warriors into a triangle formation with herself at the point where they would first contact the enemy and she carried her sword of light. The rest of her army had taken a separate road, which they hoped would take them to a place behind or to the side of the army of the three Kings and they had their orders if this was the case. Even now Sgiath tried to avoid a fight by offering the three Kings terms for a peaceful passage but this was rejected.

'You have rejected my terms,' said Sgiath, 'so your fate and that of your men is on your own heads for I will show no mercy.'

The Kings laughed. 'You and your army are only women. Do you really think you have the ability to beat us and our men? It is your blood that will stain the heather, though we might keep some of you to warm our beds.'

Without more parley, Sgiath gave the signal to attack. She and her triangle of warriors charged up the hill in tight formation whilst the army of Kings rushed to meet them in loose groups.

At first it seemed as though Sgiath's formation would cut through the army of the Kings as it had done at the valley of the Chief but this was a bigger army with many more men and soon the triangle was surrounded and fighting desperately to survive. Even Sgiath with her sword of light, which slew men like corn before the scythe, was hard-pressed.

Just as it seemed Sgiath's army would be overwhelmed by sheer weight of numbers, the other section of the Amazon warriors came round the side of the hill and charged into the flank of the army of the Kings. It was the turning point of the battle.

Caught between two forces, the Kings' army started to break and flee and were slaughtered as they ran. Sgiath gave no quarter to the three Kings who were killed by Sgiath or Enya when they tried to surrender. But to the men who had fought for the Kings Sgiath extended mercy if they surrendered their weapons and promised never to fight against her again.

So Sgiath became Queen of the three small kingdoms but this was not what she wanted.

She appointed one of her Amazon warriors to each of the three areas, each a Chieftainess in her own right. But Sgiath's mind was set on being Ard Ban Righ of all of Skye and would settle for nothing less.

Her Amazons were also happy to follow her and help her gain her ends for they knew each of them had a chance of becoming a Chieftainess or a sub-Queen or at the very least become a trusted tutor in the centres Sgiath intended to set up so that all the children would be trained in science, art and war. But all their great hopes and plans depended on Sgiath succeeding in becoming the High Queen of all Skye.

chapter twelve

Yet now Sgiath had become a source of worry and trouble to the King of the South of Skye. Her defeat of the three minor Kings had caused some fear and anger to the King and his generals.

The King decided that now was the time to use his military might against Sgiath before she became too powerful, for he knew that women were flocking to her banner but also that these women needed time to be trained, so now was the time to move against them and crush their uprising.

Sgiath, however, already realised this so she evaded direct conflict with his army but kept up a continuous and insidious campaign of guerrilla warfare and acts of sabotage against the King's forces. Small groups of her Amazons would lie in wait for sections of the King's army and then suddenly attack, causing many deaths and disruption. Then before the men could circle or engage, they fled into the deep recesses of the High Mountains they knew so well.

Sgiath, too, lost a few of her Amazon warriors in those skirmishes but very few compared to the losses of the King's men and, whilst the King's men were diverted by such a skirmish, other groups of Amazons would raid the storehouses of the King, setting fire to many of them and taking away grain and other foodstuff to supply Sgiath's followers.

Now the winter was setting in and Sgiath decided to make one large attack upon the army of the King and at the same time carry out a raid on his remaining storehouses, carrying off whatever provisions they could and setting fire to as many of the other storehouses as possible. Sgiath herself would lead the attack on the King's army, whilst Enya would lead the various groups who would ransack and burn the storehouses.

On the day Sgiath deemed right, she led the main body of her Amazons in a furious and sustained attack on a section of the King's army, knowing they would send out signals to bring the main part of the army to their aid. When the main part of the army arrived, Sgiath led her Amazons in a pre-planned retreat yet kept the King's army engaged in battle. Many died of the King's men and a few of Sgiath's Amazons, but then on a pre-arranged signal, the Amazons split into three bands of fleeing women, each taking a different route so the army of the King was unsure which band to follow. Perhaps afraid of ambush, by the time they made a decision, Sgiath's Amazons had disappeared into the mountain passes. But now runners arrived to carry the news that many storehouses had been attacked and burnt and the King's army had to return to defend the remaining stores or they might starve. So Sgiath again escaped.

Yet now her victory was dearly bought for seven of her Amazon were dead and several injured, but worst of all was Enya and two of her band were missing, perhaps captured.

chapter thirteen

giath sent out search parties to try to find out what had happened to Enya and the two other Amazons and it was a party led by Sgiath who came upon their mutilated bodies. They were not long dead but had evidently suffered greatly. Their ears and noses had been sliced off as had their breasts and other wounds and marks of torture were on their bodies.

Sgiath made a great oath on seeing the bodies, especially that of Enya who she loved like a sister, that she would inflict revenge on the King of the South of Skye and on any of his followers who stayed true to him. This she swore on the naked blade of her sword that made the oath an everlasting pledge.

All through that winter, Sgiath and her Amazons lived in caves in the High Mountains. More women joined their ranks and were trained by Sgiath, not only in the use of arms but also in skills to help them to survive. They learned the use of herbs and invocations so that they could sit or stand naked in the snow and frost or under icy streams and even to shut out pain for, as the Old Grey Magician had taught, all these are things controlled by the mind and if you can control your mind, you control your body.

Despite her training and teaching, Sgiath never forgot her final goal and her oath of vengeance so, as spring started to appear and the thanks of the people were made to the 'Sacrificial God', Sgiath made her plans and preparation to take her revenge. Yet before that, she had to carry out the burial of her beloved Enya and the other Amazons.

The bodies were carried to a sacred place of the Druids and there Enya's body was laid in a stone coffin with the two other Amazons laid on each side of her. Then the coffins were covered with stones carried there by Sgiath and her Amazons and, over the top of the cairn of rocks was laid a layer of turf. Once the cairn was closed, Sgiath went to the highest point of the cairn and placed on the turf one rowan berry from which might grow the tree that was most magical of all the trees of the Druids.

To the astonishment of all her Amazons, she watered the berry with her own tears and none had ever seen her cry before nor ever did again. Then she led all those there in an appreciation of the life of Enya with story, song and dance and Enya's favourite songs and music were said to be heard by Enya in the other world and give joy to those she had left in this one.

So all who watched saw the rituals and incantations of the Druids carried out and Enya buried and commemorated as if she had been a Queen and to many she was.

chapter fourteen

After the proper ceremonies and the burial of Enya had been carried out, Sgiath gathered together all the Amazon warriors of her band. She stood on the slope of a natural amphitheatre in the hills and spoke to them all.

'I have gathered you together to give to you the dream of Enya and myself. Enya was my soul-sister and she and I met at the very beginning of my journey and we shared the same dream. Now Enya is gone but I intend to carry on to fulfil our dream but I am sharing this dream with all of you and if you are happy to continue with me, we shall go on to make the dream come true. On the other hand, if you do not want to follow me and fight alongside me for the dream, you can leave us now.'

Having said this, Sgiath outlined the principles of their great dream.

'We will bring a land of peace and learning, a land where there is equality of justice for all whether rich or poor, male or female.

In our land, a great school of knowledge shall be set up that all who wish to learn of science and art and war can learn such knowledge regardless of whether they are rich or poor, for knowledge is found in all people whatever their tribe or position in life.

We will live and teach with nature, for with nature we can do all things, whilst against nature we kill ourselves and all mankind. What is of nature cannot be wrong.

Nature is the great beating heart of the world and from it flows the rivers and streams which are the lifeblood of the Earth and the seas and lochs are the essential organs. If we preserve them, they will preserve us. But if we destroy them, we destroy ourselves.

We will open our doors to the stranger, share with them and make them friends. We will not force a fight but neither will we shun a fight. Our doors will always be open to the needy and a share to those too old to hunt. Remember the elderly are those who fed you in your childhood days. Closer than stone to earth is the love of the coivi.

Forgive a sibling to seven times but a foster seven times seven, though blood will out.

The leaders or elders of the people will be elected by the people and a bad leader can be deposed. Leaders and elders may be male or female.

What we are fighting for is freedom for all, whether male or female and of whatever colour of skin or hair.'

Now you have heard our dream. Those of you who cannot share that dream can leave now but to those who remain, I can promise only more training and fighting, yet I believe that we shall win our battles and our dream will become a reality. But we have many streams to cross before that time comes.

Having spoken, Sgiath looked over the crowd of Amazons to see how many would leave for she feared that the road she had described of strict training and the possibility of death or severe wounds in battle might cause many to leave, although some would like the dream.

As she looked to see who was leaving, she was astonished and delighted that not one of her Amazons moved to leave but all with one voice chanted her name and 'we stay'.

So Sgiath and her Amazons united by one dream moved on to make their destiny.

chapter fifteen

efore the spring had properly set in, Sgiath led her warriors down from their caves and hidden glens in the mountains into the soft green lands of the King of the South of Skye. They destroyed the houses and barns of the people they met as they went and, if any tried to fight against them, they were killed, so of course word of their invasion was taken to the King.

He knew this was a direct challenge to his authority that he must face, yet it was a bad time for him and his army for they had been on low rations for some weeks, owing to the depredations of Sgiath and her warriors.

During the winter months, Sgiath had been training 30 of the very strongest of her Amazons in the use of a new weapon and now was the time to test it in battle. The King of the South of Skye had chosen a place to fight. He had placed his army on the slope of a hill where they could use their height to give impetus to their charge downhill upon Sgiath and her Amazons. They greatly outnumbered Sgiath's band and were sure that with the advantage of the hill, they could in their charge surround and break the triangle they expected Sgiath to form.

Sgiath's Amazons came down towards the army of the King but, to the surprise of the King, they stopped about half a mile short of where the King's army stood and formed a line of three. Behind the line of three, out of sight of the King's men, Sgiath deployed her 30 Amazons with their new weapon, the foot bow. This was a form of bow made in a composition of wood, horn and bone and could be pulled only by the very strong and fired arrows about six-foot-long, which were pointed with sharp flints or hard charred pointed wood. To use it, the person had to lie on their back with their feet raised on a rock or a hillock and placed in stirrups on the bow, pull back the arrow and string with both hands sighting along the arrow, then release the arrow which could kill a deer at a distance of half a mile or more. In the right hands, it was deadly accurate.

Sgiath gave the signal and the 30 archers released their arrows, which plunged down into the army of the King and caused many casualties. Although the bows were slow to reload and draw, a second flight of arrows also rained down upon the King's army with many more casualties and consternation spreading through in its ranks. Even as a third launch of arrows was being prepared, Sgiath led her Amazons in a charge up the hill. Then, as arrows soared over the heads of Sgiath's army, now formed into its triangle, they cut straight into the heart of the army of the King, who were still disorganised and shocked by the effects of Sgiath's new weapon. As Sgiath's triangle drove on into the army of the King, they became surrounded by his men though some of them had already given up the fight and run for safety. Then the warriors of the foot bow arrived to assist Sgiath, cutting their way into the King's men so that the ground was red with blood and covered with the dead and dying.

Now Sgiath drove forward on her own from her position at the point of the triangle and cut her way to the place where the King was fighting and rallying his men. The two met face to face. The King had a great axe with which he had killed many and Sgiath had her sword of blue light. As they began to fight, both armies drew back and watched this single combat of two heroes. It was a desperate and deadly fight, for the King was well versed in the use of his great axe and Sgiath was a master of the sword. After a time, the blows of the King became weaker and his return of the axe slower.

Sgiath laughed at him and said, 'How does it feel to fight a real warrior? I will do to you as you did to Enya and my two other warriors, for I promised revenge for them and my promises I keep.'

The King retaliated to this with a burst of energy in attack but Sgiath turned aside his axe.

With a quick stroke of her sword, she cut off the King's right ear then, as he flinched, she cut off his left ear. The King made a last desperate attempt to land a blow on Sgiath but, with a mighty blow of her sword, she cut off the head of his axe then, on the return stroke of her sword, she cut off his nose.

'Now you are as you left Enya,' said Sgiath, 'but you have more to come.'

As she said this, her sword flashed again and the belt holding the King's Feile-Mhor was severed. On the back swing, the upper part of it was cut through so that it fell to the ground and the King stood naked. Again, the sword flashed and the King screamed in agony as he was castrated. He doubled over in agony and cried to Sgiath, 'Kill me now give me at least a quick death!'

'You did not give Enya and her companions a quick death, so you do not deserve one. Now my wise women will heal your wounds and you will be chained to an oar in one of my galleys to suffer whatever time you might live.'

Then Sgiath turned to the remainder of the army of the King. 'You have seen what happened to your King. You have a choice: you can swear fealty to me as your Queen or you can be as your King.'

The King's army immediately swore fealty to Sgiath but one man stepped forward. 'I will be as my King is and row beside him in a galley,' he said. 'I am Seoras the Seannachaidh and my King and Chief was a good and honest leader. He cared for his people and I will not desert him now. Yet if you grant to my King the quick death he wishes, I will serve you and be your Seannachaidh as I was my King's and will tell truthfully your deeds in story and song.'

Sgiath looked at the man and said, 'You are a good honest and loyal friend to your King. In time, you will be the same to me for you will be my Seannachaidh and your wish is granted.' Then with one stroke of her sword she beheaded the King, giving him the quick death he desired.

Seoras did become the Seannachaidh to Sgiath and the first man in her band of Amazon warriors.

chapteR sixteen

ow Sgiath was the Queen of the South of Skye and she took over the castles and lands of the old King. She started to impose her own laws and tried to rule in a way that was fair to all her subjects. She set up chairs of judgement (Standing Stones) to which anyone who had a complaint could come and the local Chief and his Council of Elders would give a decision on how the case should be settled.

Criminals were also tried at these stones, including murderers and other serious malcontents but the judgements given took consideration of all the elements of the crime and were very pragmatic in accordance with the teachings of Sgiath, which she had learned from the knowledge of the Druids passed on to her by the Old Grey Magician.

For example, someone found guilty of murder would not necessarily be killed but, if the murdered person left a young family behind them, the murderer would be sentenced to maintain that family until the youngest person in it could support themselves. If the murderer did not support the family, he or she would be killed. However, if it was a brutal and pre-planned murder with no extenuating circumstances, the murderer would be killed in one of several ways. Sgiath ensured that her laws applied to all regardless of their portion in society and she was much respected by the people at large for her fairness to all.

chapter seventeen

ow Sgiath found out that becoming a Queen was much easier than remaining a Queen for the King of the North of Skye. Other Kings in the north and other islands were not pleased to see a woman taking what they considered to be the rightful place of a man, so they began to conspire against Sgiath and some of the greater Kings encouraged minor Kings to attack the lands and castles of Sgiath.

Sgiath and her forces had to move to many different places to avoid being captured or slain by stronger forces, yet Sgiath always looked for new ideas and built on these ideas to bring new ways of fighting and also to adapt them to peaceful uses in the future.

On one of their enforced travels, they came to a glen where a man Eachann nam t each (Hector of the horses) lived. Eachann and his family welcomed Sgiath and her band, letting them stay and giving them hospitality for several days. In that time, Sgiath saw Eachann's amazing ability with horses: how he could train them to be ridden or to pull carts and sledges but the carts and sledges they pulled were heavy, awkward things with the carts having solid wooden wheels and being very difficult to manoeuvre.

Yet Sgiath saw here an opportunity to bring something new and persuaded Eachann to show her how to ride a horse and control it with her knees so that her hands were free. She also studied the carts and sledges for she thought such knowledge would be useful at some future date.

After they moved on from that glen, Sgiath's small band of Amazon warriors increased as women from many areas came to join them. Two daughters of Eachann had joined Sgiath's band. They had the ability with horses of their father so to them Sgiath entrusted the capture and training of some of the wild Skye ponies. Sturdy beasts they were, strong and agile and very sure-footed on rough ground.

Sgiath and Eachann's daughters also trained some of the Amazons in riding and using the ponies and Sgiath added to this her own idea of using weapons such as spears and clubs from the back of the ponies. Then she used the ponies and riders as fast skirmishers to harass her enemies. She herself led many of the attacks and her mounted warriors became a terror to many of the tribes who opposed her and had never come up against this form of warfare.

However, Sgiath was not content to rest on her laurels for she knew her mounted warriors would quickly be copied by opposing forces and she wanted to maintain an edge. For this purpose, she and Eithne, one of the daughters of the Wise Woman, together with Dhuibne, the metal worker studied the clumsy cart of Hector. Between them, they made a body woven of hazel and willow rods sat on a T-shaped wooden frame of light but strong timber. The short part of the T was the axle and they also devised wheels with a central hub of birchwood and spokes to an outside rim of birchwood and Dhuibne made hoops of iron which bound the outside rim making a wheel that was strong but light. Having done this, they trained themselves and several other Amazons in the skills needed to use these chariots.

The chariots were a great success, especially in skilled hands and ensured Sgiath's victory in many battles on her journey to her dream. Each chariot could carry a charioteer and an Amazon with a supply of spears and a hand weapon – an axe, sword or club and a good supply of arrows for special short double bent bows of great power and accuracy at closer range.

Meanwhile, one of the young minor Kings saw a chance for him to kill Sgiath and take the Kingship of the South of Skye for himself. He was a very cruel and ruthless King and he felt that no woman could be ruthless enough to overcome him and his well-trained men. He spied on the movements of Sgiath, waiting for a time when her castle in the south might be held only by Sgiath herself and a small bodyguard of her Amazons. Before long, what he thought was the ideal situation for him came around, for Sgiath sent off a large part of her Amazon army to quell a minor uprising in a far-off part of her land, leaving Sgiath alone with some 50 Amazons in the castle. The King waited until he knew the Amazon army was several days' march from the castle. Then he attacked.

He and his men caught a group of the Amazon bodyguard outside the castle, killing five and injuring and capturing two. But the others in the group by skill of arms escaped from the young Kings army and got back into the castle before the gates closed barring access to the young King and his men.

'I will give you a chance of your life,' the young King shouted to Sgiath. 'If you and your Amazons lay down your arms and come out of the castle and leave this area, my men and I will let you pass safely!'

Sgiath, however, knew the character of the young King and that he would break his word without a thought. She had also seen the look that he gave his men as he made his promise.

'I will have to consider your offer,' she shouted back. 'Will you give me time before you attack to discuss it with my advisors?'

'You have two hours,' said the young King. 'Then we will attack and we will give no quarter!'

Sgiath went down from the rampart telling her warriors to be ready for an attack, which she was sure would come before the time was up. The fires were lit below the tubs of water and oil to have the contents boiling and ready and the archers checked their bows and arrows. Loose rocks had also been carried into the castle and were placed at strategic points.

Sgiath was right: barely an hour had passed when the young King launched his men in a co-ordinated attack, some carrying ladders to lay against the walls and a group with a large tree trunk to use as a battering ram against the gates. The attack was launched with great fury, men climbed the ladders laid against the walls and, at the same time, the battering ram was rammed against the door. The Amazons were ready and their archers killed and injured many of those on the ladders, then tubs of scalding hot oil and water were dashed down on top of those who had evaded the arrows.

The defenders at the door suddenly opened it as the group ran forward with the battering-ram and, unable to stop, they came straight into the castle through the door, which was promptly closed behind them before more attackers could enter. The ones who had entered were killed and five were captured by the Amazons, including a son of the young King. The attackers withdrew to lick their wounds, realising it might not be as easy as they thought to oust Sgiath and her small band from the castle.

In the morning, the young King shouted again to Sgiath. 'You have fought well but you cannot hold out against us for long. We lost men but you lost some of your Amazons and we outnumber you greatly. We can afford to lose men. But I will give another chance. We have captured two of your Amazons and my offer is this. If you come out now and surrender, I will let them and the others you have with you live. If you do not surrender, they will be tortured to death in front of your eyes!'

'I must put your offer to my Amazons and hear what they say,' replied Sgiath. 'But how can your word be trusted when you broke it already? Remember we hold five of your men including your son. If you do as you say to your captives, I will do the same and more to ours and your son.'

'This time my word will be true,' said the King. 'You have now until the sun is at its highest!'

But the young King thought that no woman could be ruthless enough to let her comrades die by torture.

Sgiath spoke to her Amazons who had all heard the offer of the Young King but they did not trust him, for they were certain that if they gave up their arms and surrendered, he would kill them by torture.

During the night, one of the Amazons who was a good runner had slipped out of the castle to run all the way to where the other Amazons were and tell them of the siege but it would take at best two days for them to come back to the castle, so they had to hold out till then.

Sgiath went back up on to the ramparts before the sun reached its height and shouted to the young King, 'My Amazons and I have talked about your offer and we have not reached an agreement. Some wish to know if you will give them a definitive oath upon your naked sword and on your life that you will carry out your promises.'

The young King called back, 'That is easily done. I will swear now on my naked sword and on my life that I will do as I said.'

Sgiath noted the ambiguity in the last part of his words but shouted back, 'I will speak to my Amazons again to see if we can agree. Give us time to talk until the sun's shadows move round to quarter eve.'

The King agreed but said, 'You must give your answer then!'

Once again Sgiath talked to her Amazons but their opinions had not changed. They did not trust the King. Again, before the time was up, Sgiath went on to the ramparts and called to the King.

'I have spoken with my Amazons and they would like one thing added and that is that we exchange prisoners before we leave the castle.'

'No,' shouted the King. 'You are only trying to prolong the time. I will now carry out my word.'

He made a signal to his men and they dragged to the front of the castle the two Amazons they had captured. They were naked and bloodstained, yet each had an air of dignity and contempt for their captors.

'I tell you now,' said Sgiath, 'if you do as you threatened with my Amazons, your men and your son with suffer more.'

'No woman is ruthless enough to do that,' shouted back the King. 'Now listen to them scream.'

'Hold your hand,' shouted Sgiath, 'and look up here.'

The King saw his son and four others of his army taken naked onto the ramparts of the castle with their hands tied behind their backs and a rope attached to each ankle. As the King and his men watched, the five prisoners were lowered over the ramparts, suspended by the ropes on their ankles in a spread-eagled way with their backs against the wall.

'You see your men and your son,' cried Sgiath. 'They are alive and well now. I am willing to exchange them for my two Amazons but if you refuse my offer and torture and kill my Amazons, then the same will happen to your men and your son. But you can still save them. What man would see his son die this way?'

'You cannot do it!' the King shouted back. 'No woman could!' and with his own hand he made the first cut of torture on one of the Amazons.

As Sgiath saw the torture commence, she shouted again to the King. 'If you stop the torture of my comrades now, I will spare your men and your son but if you kill my Amazons by torture, your soldiers will die the same way.'

The King would not listen to Sgiath and signalled to his men to continue with the torture. Sgiath and her Amazons watched as their comrades were slowly cut to pieces in ways intended to inflict the greatest suffering. When death finally released the women from their agony, Sgiath stepped to their ramparts of her castle and with her own hand, she castrated the first of the men hanging over the ramparts. Then her Amazons inflicted the most painful cuts they could devise on the man, slicing open his belly so that his entrails poured out and over his face. As he screamed and writhed in his final agonies, they cut the ropes on his ankles and he plunged down the side on the castle and crashed on the rocks below. The same treatment was meted out to the other three captives but when it came to the son of the King, Sgiath called out to him again.

'I will give you back your son,' she said, 'if you and your men will leave my land and swear an oath never to fight against me again.'

'I will not do that,' shouted back the King. 'No woman would dare to kill my son.'

'So be it,' said Sgiath, 'but remember it was you who condemned your son.'

Then the same was done to the son of the King as had been done to his men and his broken body lay on the rocks. The King went mad with rage and launched a great attack, hoping to overcome Sgiath by sheer weight of numbers regardless of the losses of his men. So fierce was the assault and so great the number of his men, it began to appear that Sgiath and her Amazons would be swamped and suffer death and torture as had those captured before them.

Just as it seemed that all was lost, there appeared behind the army of the King the Amazons who had been away at another part of Sgiath's Kingdom. Without delay and to the surprise of the King's army, they launched a counter attack from the rear and as the King's men turned to meet them, Sgiath led her Amazons from the castle in an attack that drove through the King's army and, caught between two forces, his men started to break and run.

Sgiath cut her way through the fleeing men till she reached the place where the King fought on and tried to rally his troops.

'No man who would sacrifice his son and his men is fit to be a King,' said Sgiath. 'You have brought your death on your own head.'

'One of us shall die,' replied the King, 'but it will not be me' and he swung his great axe, hoping to end the fight with one blow.

Sgiath sidestepped the axe and before the King could recover and swing again, with one strong blow of her sword she cut the haft of the axe so that the King was left but the stub of it between his hands. Just as realisation dawned on him, Sgiath reversed the swing of her blade, cutting open his belly so that his intestines poured out between his frantically clutching fingers. He fell to his knees.

'Now you know something of what your son and men suffered,' said Sgiath, 'but I will be kinder to you than you were to them.' One more swing of her sword and the King's head was removed from his body and rolled down amongst the feet of those around.

When the remainder of the Army of the King saw this, they threw down their arms and submitted to Sgiath. She granted them their lives but they had to swear on her naked sword that they would never take up arms against her and if she called on them to help in any of her future plans, they must do so. All of the survivors were happy to do this and were allowed to return to whence they came as free men.

Once again, Sgiath appointed one of her Amazons to be the ruler of the area once known as the realm of the young King.

chapter eighteen

After Sgiath conquered the King of the South of Skye and became Queen in his stead, she arranged a parley with her sister, Aoife. They arranged to meet at a place known to both of them, a quiet hollow in the hills with a waterfall at one end and a stream running from it, a very pleasant and peaceful spot surrounded by trees and deep heather. A corrie amongst the hills.

On their meeting there, Sgiath offered to Aoife the regency of the South of Skye. Aoife would reign as the representative of Sgiath and would implement the laws and rules of justice for all that Sgiath put into place in each area she conquered.

Aoife refused to act as regent and implement Sgiath's laws of equality. She said she would only rule as a real Queen and would impose her own laws and her own form of justice. Sgiath could not agree to this and told Aoife that she either accepted the regency and Sgiath's laws or she got nothing.

Aoife laughed in the face of Sgiath, saying, 'I have made my own plans, dear sister, and you are not included in them. It's a pity you have to die soon.'

As she said it, she clapped her hands and from the trees came ten of her men to surround Sgiath, ready to kill her. Sgiath gave a whistle and out from the heather and the gullies came ten of her Amazons.

'As you can see, sister dear, I had my own plans and knew not to trust you. You and your men can leave in peace or I and my Amazons shall kill your men and send you back to your followers as a beaten and shamed false leader. You would, of course, be physically beaten by my Amazons but not severely wounded.

Aoife realised her men were no match for the Amazons and Sgiath and she feared the physical beating promised to her.

'My men and I will leave in peace and leave our weapons as a sign of good faith, for I know you would not allow us to take them. Yet I will not give up my fight against you.' So said Aoife and walked away with her men but the hatred in her heart for Sgiath was even greater than before.

chapter nineteen

giath soon realised that the King of the North of Skye was behind urging other Kings to attack and harass her and she decided that now was the time to move against him, when he was partly discredited after Sgiath's victory over the young King, his protégé. Gathering her Amazon warriors together and supplementing them with men from the young King's army, Sgiath marched north to give battle to the army of the King of the North of Skye. However, Sgiath was wise enough to know that she was still outnumbered by his army, so she sent one of her raiding parties to attack villages to divert his attention. She had scouts out who would keep her informed of the movements of those divisions of the King's army so that they could be ambushed and annihilated by Sgiath's fast-moving assault parties.

Soon, the King of the North of Skye realised that Sgiath's tactic of dividing his forces to defend the villages was gradually taking away the strength of his army and he decided to stop trying to defend the villages, instead forcing Sgiath to face his army directly in battle. Now his army marched as a single unit, searching for Sgiath and her army. If they came across skirmishes of Sgiath's army, they were overwhelmed by numbers and no quarter was given to them.

After this, Sgiath changed her tactics. She left evidence of the movement of her army to be found by the King's men, hoping to draw his army to an area she wanted to fight in and which would give her an advantage, for she knew she must take every advantage she could as her army was still outnumbered. So she drew the army of the King to a glen in the west of Skye where she felt the lay of the ground served her tactics and there, on the broad flat fields beside the river, she drew up the main force of her army. In the slopes above the flat fields, she hid her bowman (both of the foot bow and the hand bow). She hoped when the King's army saw her women in battle array on the flat fields, they would trust in their superior numbers and charge into what would become a horseshoe with the wings that would outflank and overpower the King's men.

So they prepared and waited for the King's army to arrive. Their scouts told them he was not far away and hot on their trail.

chapteʀ twenty

ow the army of the King of the North of Skye marched into the glen but, to the annoyance of Sgiath, it did not rush into an assault on her Amazon warriors but stopped a fair distance away from the main body of her soldiers. Sgiath realised that this was a chance to hold talks with the King as the Druids taught: 'Never force a fight, never run from a fight, always try to talk before a fight.'

So with two of her Amazon warriors, Sgiath went forward towards the army of the King and he in turn came forward with two of his men, all of them showing by their open hands that they had not come to fight.

As they met halfway between the two opposing armies, Sgiath and the King studied each other. The King saw a young, well-built woman more handsome than beautiful but with a well-toned body, full-breasted, narrow-waisted, with wide child-bearing hips, yet at the same time strong and muscular. Sgiath saw a man strongly built, just past his prime but one who could be a formidable opponent. He had a fine and firm looking face with bright, intelligent eyes and a sword scar on his right cheek.

'Let us talk,' said the King, 'for this could be a killing ground for many men and women without any good from it and it is a shame to waste lives when it is not needed.'

'You have raised other smaller Kings against me,' replied Sgiath, 'and every one of them my Amazons and I have defeated, yet now you say you do not want to waste lives. This matter must be clarified, for only one of us can rule and my army and I are determined that it will be me.'

'You and your army may think this,' replied the King, 'but you are against greater odds and better strategists now than you have been before. You have set your army up in such a way as to draw us into a horseshoe, thinking that we would attack the centre but I have deployed men behind the ridges at each side of the glen so that we in fact outflank you. Even still, I will offer you a solution now. Withdraw your army and return to the south of Skye, giving me your word that you will never invade the north again, and I will promise not to invade the south, nor to assist in any plots against you. Otherwise, we can give the signal and the slaughter will begin. However, it might end.'

Sgiath thought long before she answered, for she realised if the King had outflanked her as he said then many would die and no one could foretell who might be victorious in such a blood bath.

'I have thought over all you have said and I too would be ashamed to throw away lives needlessly. I have another solution to offer you. Let us meet in single combat in the way that was honoured by our ancestors, using any weapons you choose. Whichever of us is victorious will be the King or Queen of all Skye and our armies will be bound by our agreement on this that the only blood spilled will ours,' said Sgiath.

'That is indeed a noble thought,' answered the King. 'I shall meet you willingly in single combat and the weapons I choose will be the great sword and the short spear. Let us now tell our armies of our decision and then we shall meet as heroes should and to the victor will go the crown.'

So the King went back to his army and told his generals of decision that had been made. They agreed to its terms and praised him for his courage and care for his men. Sgiath also went back to her army and told her Amazon warriors and her generals of the agreement made and, while some of the Amazons said they would have preferred to fight, they too agreed to the terms. Then both the King and Sgiath prepared themselves for combat.

Sgiath gave a last sharpening to the edge of the great sword she had taken from the leader of the cannibals and checked the short spear called Gae-Bolg that the Old Grey Magician had given to her. She made sure that her Earrasaid was belted and buckled firmly so that it would not hinder her in the fight.

The King also sharpened his great sword which, like Sgiath's, gleamed silver blue in the sun. He made sure his short spear was sharp and ready and that his Feile-Mhor (Phillimore) was securely fastened.

Then as the sun rose towards its zenith, each of them walked to the flat area called the Island, which was really a peninsula in the river, and their followers lined up on the opposite banks of the river where all had a good view of the combatants. The King and Sgiath walked out to the centre of the flat Island and each checked the other's weapons. Then they withdrew to opposite sides of the Island.

As Sgiath stood there waiting for the blast of the horn to herald the start of combat, she looked up the glen to the flat-topped mountains called Sealbh Mor's Sealbh Bhig (the greater and lesser charmed mountains) and, as she did so, it seemed as though the mountains smiled on her and gave her a promise that her dream would come true.

Then the horn sounded and all her senses had to be concentrated on winning victory over her opponent. The King attacked with great fury, trying out Sgiath's ability in defence and she was hard pushed to ensure he did not overwhelm her with the speed and skill of his attack. Their swords clashed and rang, grating against each other, sending showers of sparks into the air as the bright blades locked and grated, yet the King did not get the result he wished, for Sgiath diverted the frenzy of his attack and parried his blows by using her skill to evade and divert his thrusts and slashes.

As their trial by single combat went on, the King felt his age starting to slow his feet and lessen the vigour of his blows. Sgiath felt the slackening of his energy and she began to press him and increase the power in her own strokes. But he was still a formidable opponent and both of them were bleeding from small injuries, so close had been the combat.

But now the King decided to summon up the last of his remaining resources to launch a desperate attack upon Sgiath, hoping that he could sustain it long enough to penetrate her defences and land a mortal wound. To his amazement and despair, Sgiath did not only match his assault but she met it with such an attack of her own that he was driven on to the defensive. In the midst of her attack, she used a piece of supreme skill to sweep his sword from his hand. As he tried to bring his short spear into play, with a backslash of her sword, she cut the head off the spear and, in the same movement, turned the backslash into a forward sweep that would have taken the head of the King off his shoulders. But at the moment before the edge of the sword bit into the base of his neck, she turned the blade so that the flat instead of the edge impacted on his neck.

The King dropped to the ground, dazed, and waited for the final flow to end his life but it did not come. Sgiath gave her hand to the King and

helped him to his feet and, as his senses returned
to him, she said, 'You have shown yourself to be
a brave and honourable man and do not deserve
to die. I will tell you of my plan and dream for the
future and if you are willing to be a part of it, you
can join with me to carry it out. If you do not wish
to assist me then I will exile you to a remote island
to live out whatever remains of your life.'

'Tell me your dream,' said the ex-King, 'and it
could well be that our ideas can be combined, for
I am weary of always fighting to hold my position.
I have no other life than the one I have always led
from the time I was a boy at my father's knee but
I have always felt there must be other ways to live.'

'When I was a girl being trained by the Old
Grey Magician,' said Sgiath, 'he told me that I was
destined to be a Queen. I had to find my own way.
I realised I did not want to become a great Queen
just by fighting other Kings or Queens but I could
become famous all over our world by becoming
not only the greatest warrior of all but by teaching
all the heroes and scholars of art, science and war.
So this became my dream and I now want to set
up a college of learning where all who wish can
come and learn not only from me but from other
tutors – tutors who I have picked and who share my
dream. Those who come to learn must learn science,
art and war. Some will be better in one subject than
others but all must have the feeling and knowledge
of every subject so that they can be complete.'

'That is a great dream,' replied the ex-King. 'I would like to be a part of your dream and I promise you, if you set up your place of learning, I would be faithful to you. If you will have me, I would perhaps be a tutor for I have knowledge of war and have always loved the arts, although of science I have little knowledge.'

'You have shown me that you are well-versed in war and you are also a great swordsman. On the arts, I must take your word and I already know of a man great in science so I will be glad to have you swear faithfulness to me and to have you join me in putting together a place of learning. I promise you it will not be long in coming,' said Sgiath. 'Then we must hope we can succeed in carrying out my dream.'

There and then on the field of combat, Sgiath and the ex-King struck hands and exchanged blood on their bargain so both were bound. Then Sgiath took from the King his armlet of Majesty and she was hailed by both armies as the Queen of all Skye. So the first part of her dream was fulfilled and she looked ahead to carry out the second part of the prophecy of the Old Grey Magician. Though she knew it was a long hard road that lay ahead, she felt inside herself a great new excitement and an urge to start to follow her dream and see it through.

But little did she know of all the twists that fate had in store for her and her vision. Even if she had known, it would not have turned her from the road she had started on.

chapter twenty-one

giath started her rule of Skye
by visiting each district and, in
each one, she placed one of her
Amazons as Chief of that area. She
also set out rules to be followed
by each district but gave each the
right to make their own local laws
within the overall central rules. One of her main
innovations was that, after one year of her rule,
the people would have the right to elect their own
Chief and committee of Elders, even if it meant her
appointee was deposed. Every resident in the area
would have a vote, male or female, after they had
undergone the Rites of Passage. Both males and
females would have equal rights and, if a woman
was as good as a man, they would be given same
accolade. This was unheard of and, to many men,
at first unthinkable but Sgiath had been taught
this as one of the rules of the Druids by the Old
Grey Magician and she enforced it. Very quickly, it
became accepted all over Skye.

Now she began her task of setting up a great
college of learning, where all who genuinely wished
to learn could apply, whether rich or poor, and
if they passed the tests for entry they would be

welcomed and taught. She looked for a place to base her college, it would be a remote glen with the sea at its foot and mountain and clefts around. It would need only small houses for buildings as most of the teaching would be done in nature with the sky as roof and the earth as floor.

Her first task was to find and persuade the very best in arts and science to come and teach in her colleges for, although she knew she was the greatest warrior in all forms of arms and the most skilled in war, she was not the best in things such as healing, Bardic lore, science and Druidism and only the best would do for her college. She approached her old mentor, the Old Grey Magician, to gain his advice and experience in those areas in which she was deficient and listened to his words of wisdom.

'You will find,' he said, 'that many of the best people of the arts and science will not be willing to stay permanently with your school but most will be willing to come for short times to check the progress of your pupils and the validity of the teachers. Most, if they will not come themselves, will nominate a trainee of their own as a teacher. Even you yourself must allow your best warriors to teach and you can monitor the teaching and pick those you will personally instruct in the arts of war. If you set up your college in this way and ensure that all pupils study all the arts until they find the ones in which they excel so that they can concentrate on them, your college will be renowned in every country till its time is past.'

'But how shall I be sure of who is best in each of the arts?' asked Sgiath.

'Listen to the stories of the people,' replied the Old Grey Magician. 'Already you have a start, for you know you are the best warrior, Donran is the best healer and I am the best magician and each of us knows others who have their own gifts, be it Bardic, scientific or artistic. So start with what you know and gather from there until you have the finest tutors of all. Remember the best tutors are not always the best in their particular field but are the ones who can impart the knowledge they have to others.'

'I thank you for your wise words,' said Sgiath, 'and I will act upon them. Will you as the greatest of all magicians and bearer of many types of knowledge be a tutor in my college?'

'No,' replied the Old Grey Magician, 'but I will be happy to monitor my nominee for the post and his pupils and if at any time you need me, I shall be there.'

chapter twenty-two

ow began Sgiath's time of searching for those most able to teach. First of all, she allowed the various regions she had set out to settle for one year, then to hold elections to appoint their own leaders and council of Elders. To her great delight, the vast majority of the regions voted in leaders who had been appointed by Sgiath, each with a council of five Elders who held in their minds the local tradition and history, so Sgiath was content. Where her nominee was not voted in as leader, she gave them the choice to return to her own headquarters or remain in the area they had ruled for a year. Most of them came back to Sgiath's headquarters, though they were very few, but one or two stayed on in the belief that they could help the region to flourish and they enjoyed living in that area.

Having seen her land settle down with a sense of stability established, Sgiath travelled over her own and other kingdoms, firstly to find the place which would be the seat of her college of learning and also to persuade the best of each branch of the arts to teach in her college.

Finding the place was not so difficult, for it was already in her mind and in her dreams, so when she came to Lomhar-sgil in Gleann-na-Gall, she knew it was the place. Even the name was right – the place of the magic (or shining) art – and it was found in the glen of the stranger. Sgiath took this as the final definitive sign that this was her place of learning and now she could tell those she approached as tutors where her college would be. This would be a help in persuading them to come and once she had gathered the tutors, the scholars and heroes would surely follow.

Now her quest for tutors began in earnest. The first person she wished to try to join her in her college was Donran, the greatest healer of all, a man who lived with and in nature. He communed with the plants and the streams, the animals and the insects and even had the wisdom of the bees. Him she must find and hopefully persuade him to be her tutor in the art of healing. However, Donran was not easily found, unless he wished to be.

After searching fruitlessly for several days, Sgiath and her small band were nearly at the stage of giving up when, as they stirred in the morning, Donran appeared. As always, he was naked as nature made him.

'I have watched you search for me these last few days. I wondered why for I can see you are not ill, nor have I heard of any sickness in your kingdom, so why do you search for me? It must be something of importance to you,' he said to Sgiath.

'Indeed it is,' said Sgiath. 'I am setting up a college of learning where all who wish to learn and can pass a test for entry can be tutored in art, science and war. I seek the best in these subjects to teach in my college, so I have come to you, for you are greatest in the art of healing, so I would have you as the tutor of healing.'

'It is a great dream you have,' said Donran, 'and I feel I should be part of it but I shall not tie myself to tutoring for more than six months whilst your college becomes known. After that time, I will return to my own ways, but I will give to the college one whom I have tutored myself and he or she will carry on my teaching. If they need me for a short time, I will be available. If you are willing to have me on those terms, then I will be your first tutor in the art of healing.'

'Gladly I accept you on your terms,' replied Sgiath, 'for you are the greatest of all healers and I wish only the best. I know the one you will nominate to continue your work will be worthy of trust you will place on them.'

So the agreement was made and hands struck, which was a more committed and trustworthy oath than any written word.

Now Sgiath felt the time had come for her to start her college for she had her main tutors.

For the healing arts, she had Donran and his appointee. For science and magic, she had the Old Grey Magician and his appointee. For storytelling and genealogy, she had Seoras the Seannachaidh, who also was versed in the Bardic arts. She herself would teach the arts of war with the ex-King of the North of Skye, Gavran, as her appointee when she was unable to tutor, which could happen for many reasons.

chapter twenty-three

Already the fame of Sgiath had spread to many countries and she sent some of her Amazon warriors to many of the countries in the Celtic Empire to act as agents for her college of arts and war and to persuade heroes and scholars of those countries to come to Skye for their tuition. Yet she was still beset by people at home who were envious of her achievements and tried to upset her plans.

Chief amongst those who harassed her was her own sister, Aoife, who led attacks on parts of Sgiath's kingdom and this was a great annoyance to Sgiath. Although she could have repelled Aoife's attacks and killed her, Sgiath had a *Geisa* placed on her by the Old Grey Magician that she would not kill or seriously injure her sister. Sgiath would not break her *Geisa*.

Now, however, she had a greater threat to overcome, for word had come to her that several lords and Kings in the north of Scotland and other countries were preparing a fleet of ships to invade Skye and to kill Sgiath and her Amazons, for they felt it was wrong and a betrayal of their manhood to have a Queen with female warriors reigning in any country, even worse to start a college to

train men in art and war. No woman could outdo
or teach a man, so they combined their forces to
eliminate this upstart. Their fleet of ships, filled
with fully trained and armed men, presented a great
threat to Sgiath and one that she must overcome.

She decided that her best chance lay in
gathering a fleet herself to attack at sea, hoping
the element of surprise would work in her favour.
Once her plan was formed, she acted on it as
quickly as possible and soon had ships to carry
her and her Amazons. She knew she was greatly
outnumbered, yet also knew her ships were lighter,
faster and more manoeuvrable than those of the
invading fleet.

When the enemy ships were sighted, she and
her Amazon warriors sailed out to battle the fleet
of the Kings. Sgiath had prepared a plan of action
that utilised the speed and manoeuvrability of her
ships but also used the Amazon foot bows, which,
although not accurate when fired from a ship, could
carry flaming arrows over a long distance and some
must hit and hopefully set fire to some of the Kings'
ships. The plan was partly successful and did set
alight two or three ships but the majority of the
arrows plunged into the sea. As the ships rolled in
the waves, the arrows became more of a danger to
the ships they were fired from than the ones they
were aimed at, so Sgiath stopped using them. Now
at closer quarters, the heavier and stronger ships of

the fleet of the Kings were managing to ram and sink the lighter ships of Sgiath's fleet, despite their speed and manoeuvrability. Sgiath knew that defeat loomed ahead and the balance had swung in favour of the fleet of the Kings but she and her Amazons fought on.

At this time, the Old Grey Magician was sitting naked in the small cave behind Eas-na-Seallaidh (The Waterfall of Sight). As he gazed into it, through the water he saw Sgiath's ships attacking the great fleet of the Kings and realised it was a brave but hopeless task.

'I must help my former apprentice,' he thought, 'for she has become great and can be greater.' Without further thought, he came from behind the waterfall, swimming through the pool of cleansing. As he did so, he invoked the assistance of the God of Water and of Air to assist him in the task he had put upon himself. Turning into a seabird, the Old Grey Magician flew into the air, heading southwards to where the sea-battle raged.

As he flew over the battle, he could see that while Sgiath's ships were fewer than those of the Kings, they were faster and more manoeuvreable but the greater number of the ships of the Kings were overpowering and ramming and sinking Sgiath's fleet despite the bravery and skill of the Amazons.

He flew directly to the ship that Sgiath commanded and, landing on it, turned back to his own shape and said to Sgiath, 'Would you like my help?'

'Gladly I will accept your offer of help,' said Sgiath, 'for I know your powers and have belief in you.'

'You have accepted my offer,' replied the Old Grey Magician. 'To help me carry it out, you must tie a length of cloth to the bow of each of your ships.' Then he turned again into the seabird and flew off to a rock just off the coast which could be covered by the sea at high tide. Standing naked on the rock, he cast offerings to the sea and made his incantation to the Blue Men of the Minch.

'Blue men of the Minch, my cousins of the sea, listen as I call to you and answer to my plea. I'll give you a game to play. I'm sure you will enjoy for I will show you how. Big ships you can destroy'

Suddenly Blue Men of the Minch appeared all round the rock on which the Old Grey Magician stood, and together they said:

> You call to put on us a task
> We'll do whatever you may ask
> You say it's something must be done
> And give us sport and lot of fun

The Old Grey Magician answered:

> To sink some ships below the tide
> A group must catch all on one side

CHAPTER TWENTY-THREE

> Then pull the ship below the waves
> And let them moulder in their graves
> But ships with cloth upon their bow
> You must not touch them anyhow

The Blue Men of the Minch answered:

> We hear the message that you give
> That some will die and some will live
> But with your words you set us free
> To be the Masters of the Sea

The Blue Men of the Minch swam off and attacked the ships of the Kings. Rearing out of the water on one side of the ships, they would grasp its gunwhale and pull it down till water rushed in and sank the ship. Soon the sea was full of sinking ships and drowning men, for the Blue Men gave no mercy.

Sgiath was left the victor of the Great Sea Battle with the assistance of the Old Grey Magician, yet he himself was not totally happy for he knew he had released the powers of Blue Men of the Minch and how they might use them no one knew.

Only two prisoners were brought back to Skye by Sgiath's warriors and they were taken to her castle for her to determine their fate.

chapter twenty-four

hen the two who had been captured were brought before Sgiath, she looked well upon them and asked, 'Who are you and why did you fight against me?'

The tallest of them answered, 'I am Hagar – Hagar the Slaughterer. With my great axe I have killed many men and all warriors quail before me. I fought you because my King said I would get great reward in spoils and women when we defeated you.'

'We did not quail before you, neither I nor my warriors,' replied Sgiath, 'and you are the ones who were conquered.'

She turned to the other captive who had the red-gold hair of the Celts and said to him, 'Who are you and why did you fight against me?'

'I am Conran the Harper. When I play the harp, all men stop to listen for my music is magical and puts a trance on anyone who hears it. Even the birds stop singing in the trees and gather round to listen to my music for it is the music of all nature. It is my gift.'

'Why then did you fight against me?' asked Sgiath.

Conran replied, 'I fight only for death. I join in with whoever will take me and I always hope that death will come. I would welcome it but it does not come.'

Sgiath thought for a moment then said to them, 'Have you ever known love?'

'I,' said Hagar, 'have loved hundreds of women. I know what love is; no woman ever went away unsatisfied from the bed of Hagar.'

Sgiath shook her head. 'You have never known love!'

'I have known love,' said Conran. 'When I was a young man, I met and lived in love with a beautiful young girl. Our happiness together was great and love was a cloak around us. Then one night we were sleeping in an encampment when noises awoke us. I went out to see what was wrong. Raiders had attacked us and were killing men, women and children and as I went out to fight them, my beloved came behind me and got a spear in her back that was meant for me. I went mad. A red mist came upon me and I killed and killed till all had fled or lay dead. But my beloved was dead and so was I in spirit. Ever since then, I have fought wherever and whoever I could, always trying to find death so that I could join my love but I have never found it.'

'Truly this man has loved,' said Sgiath, 'and knows what love is. I too will know the great love of one man but we will be parted and will not meet again in this world. Play for us the clarsach. Let us hear what magic you have in the harp.'

Conran picked up the harp and played and, as he played, it was as if a trance came upon all in that place as though they were under a spell. The birds stopped singing and gathered round to listen. Such music had never been heard before or since. Conran played on and on and it was as though a great dream of sleep came on everyone. When he stopped all awoke in an instant with the beauty of their dream still upon them.

'Truly you are a great harpist,' said Sgiath, 'and you play for the love you have known. She is in all its joy and grief and sorrow, you deserve your peace.'

Turning again to Hagar, she said, 'You know not what love is. You deserve to live what little time remains to you.' With one swift slice of her dagger, she castrated him and told her Amazons to take him to the kitchens to let the physician heal his wound, then put him as a slave on all the dirty work or tie him to an oar in a galley.

Conran was taken down to the shore and the Amazons staked him out naked and spread-eagled between four posts. They lit a fire near to him and, as it died down to red hot embers, Sgiath herself lifted out the hottest of the embers and placed them on Conran's chest around his heart, until it swelled and burst and Conran died.

Sgiath said, 'Surely this man knew love and gave love and now he is with his love and their love will last forever.'

chapter twenty-five

he news of the Great Sea Battle spread to all parts of the Celtic Empire and heroes and scholars from many nations came to join Sgiath's college to learn from her and her tutors. All were welcomed and given the chance to pass the entrance tests no matter whether they were rich or poor, male or female or had skin of different hues.

Yet some of those who came to the college of Sgiath came not to learn but to try to show their own powers were greater than those of Sgiath or her tutors. They would challenge the tutor of their own particular art. One of the earliest challengers was a great magician of the Celtic Teutonic (German) tribe and he challenged the Old Grey Magician. The challenge was of course accepted and the two opponents walked towards each other at the side of the river that flowed through the valley of the place of the magic (or shining) art – the Old Grey Magician walking up the river from the college, the challenger known as Thurda coming down the river from the entrance to the glen.

Before they met, Thurda pointed at a bush and it burst into flames but the Old Grey Magician laughed and pointed his staff at a rock, from which sprang a spout of water that extinguished the fire. Thurda turned into a snake which tried to strike its poisonous fangs into the leg of the Old Grey Magician but he picked up the snake by the tail and turned it into a hazel staff which he threw into the river. As it hit the surface, it turned back into Thurda who now hurled at the Old Grey Magician a bolt of energy, which scorched the ground it passed over. But the Old Grey Magician merely held out his hand as if it were a shield and the bolt of energy turned back in it tracks and hit a stone beside Thurda, which shattered into a thousand fragments. Thurda was shocked and frightened for he realised his powers were nothing compared to those of the Old Grey Magician.

He bowed now before him, saying, 'You are indeed the greatest magician of all and you deserve to be the tutor of magic in Sgiath's college. I would be pleased to learn at your feet.'

'You will not learn at my feet,' said the Old Grey Magician, 'for you have shown yourself to be over-conceited of the little magic you have. I will put you on an island where you will live the remainder of your life. However, your name will not be forgotten for the island will be called Hirta, for I see you are a disciple of Thurda, the daughter of the Goddess.'

Most of the people who came to the college of Sgiath wished only to sit the test that would give them a place to learn from the great tutors, yet every one of them had to sit the tests in every discipline taught in arms, in art and in science. They did not have to be great in all of them but had to be willing to learn and their strong points would be further enhanced whilst in their weaker subjects, they would at least appreciate the skills involved and have some understanding of each subject.

chapter twenty-six

owever, problems still beset Sgiath. Her sister, Aoife, kept harassing outlying parts of Skye with her small band of warriors, knowing that Sgiath would not kill or seriously injure her because of the *Geisa* the Old Grey Magician had placed on her. At times, Sgiath's anger was so great that she wanted to fight and kill her own sister but somehow she restrained herself and waited for the hero who would come and rid her of the threat of Aoife.

Now there came to the college a hero of Austria, a giant of a man with a gentle face and an enquiring mind. When he was put to the test, Sgiath was surprised at his lack of skill in arms but great skill in the arts – painting, colouring and Bardic lore.

She was intrigued and asked him why he had come. 'Was it,' she asked, 'to gain greater skill in arms or was there some other reason?'

Jurghas replied, 'I wish no greater skill in arms. All my life because of my size I have been regarded as a hero and that is not what I want. I have come to your college to learn from your tutor, whose work I have seen, the art of enamelling on bronze

and gold, iron, wood and stone, for my dream is to
be known for such work.'

'That is a hard-learned skill you seek,' said
Sgiath, 'but if that is what you most desire then
that shall be your main learning here. But like all
others you must study all the subjects we teach, for
a spread of knowledge is good to have. Also, you
have good knowledge of painting and colouring
and you can pass this knowledge to others around
you. I hope your time here will be fruitful and your
hopes come true and your skill becomes great.'

So Jurghas of Austria became a pupil in the
college of Sgiath but, to his surprise, his first lesson
in enamelling was to make charcoal to fire the
furnace in which the pots of enamel were melted.
He was shown how to select the best logs of birch
and beech and other woods, how to stack them in
the sealed containers they were slowly charred in
and, until he perfected his charcoal making, he was
not allowed to use the furnace to melt the special
sands and pigments to make enamel.

He was, however, a very ardent pupil and
despite setbacks, he persevered and became skilled
in charcoal making. Then he had to learn the art
of burning the charcoal in the furnace so that the
ingredients of the enamel were heated to the right
temperature and for the right time, so that it could
be poured into the design carved in the object to
be decorated, whether it was bronze, gold or silver,

wood or stone – perhaps a sword hilt, sheath, an armlet or Torque. It would then be polished to its final beauty.

For a year and a day, he worked in the college, acquiring knowledge but also giving some of his own so that his knowledge of colours and painting inspired others to experiment and find more colours of enamel. However, at the end of the year and a day, Jurghas went to Sgiath and said, 'I have worked in your college with your tutors and have learned many things. Now I wish to return to my own land and there to set up a place to make enamelled brooches, Torques, armlets, sword hilts and sheaths, which will be hailed by all the world. I would like to go with your blessing.'

Sgiath looked at him standing before her and said, 'You have done well here and my tutors have told me of your progress. But they also say that you should stay for at least another year to help you perfect your skills for, if you go now, you will not attain the peak of workmanship which you deserve. Nevertheless, if you must go now, you go with my blessing.'

Jurghas replied, 'I will go now for I feel my time has come and I will set up my works at Bibracte and I will make the best enamel in the world.'

'You may go as I said with my blessing,' said Sgiath, 'but your enamel, though good, will never be the best. Surely it is worth to stay another year and then you might attain your goal.'

'No,' said Jurghas. 'I will go now and take my chance.'

So Jurghas of Austria left the college of Sgiath but many more came.

chapter twenty-seven

rom Ireland came Fergus of the short spear, a hero who was regarded in Ireland as the greatest exponent of the short spear in all the world, and maybe further. But as he said when he came to the 'land of the shadows' and challenged Sgiath, he felt like a child being taught a lesson by a parent. He had to concede defeat with his own chosen weapon.

When he returned to Ireland, he told other heroes of his humiliation at the hands of Sgiath and how he had to serve her and attend her college for a year and a day. Yet he also said how much he had learned in that time and the other heroes listened to him and many went to the college of Sgiath, including Ferdiad, the friend and fellow hero of Cuchullin.

When Ferdiad sailed from Ireland to Skye, he bore in his heart a certainty that he could conquer Sgiath, for no women could stand against a great hero such as he was accounted to be and he would bring Sgiath to Ireland as his subject. He might even take over the Kingship of Skye... So went his dreams.

Reality is often far different from dreams as Ferdiad was to discover. He landed on Skye and made his way to the college of Sgiath and challenged her to fight with his chosen weapon, the sword, a weapon with which he was esteemed a master, perhaps as good as or even better than Cuchullin.

Ferdiad and Sgiath met in combat on the level sward at the college, when the swords first met and clashed, Ferdiad discovered to his astonishment that Sgiath's wrist was as strong as his and her sword arm was as fast as his own. Their meeting was a sight to behold, as each strived to gain the advantage but cuts and lunges were parried and the swords clashed and rang, with sparks flying from their blades as they rasped together. Both the combatants appeared to be equally skilled, too, in avoiding the other's attacks by the use of skilful footwork and leaps to carry them out of danger. The watching heroes gasped in awe at the skill being shown and applauded every move in attack and defence.

As the fight went on, suddenly Sgiath increased the speed and ferocity of her attack and Ferdiad was forced to defend. Before he fully understood what was happening, he found himself on his back with Sgiath's sword point under his chin. He had to submit or die so submit he did and had to serve under Sgiath for a year and a day in her college.

At the end of that time, Ferdiad requested permission from Sgiath to stay on for a longer period of time, for his thirst for knowledge was great and he was always willing to learn. Sgiath gladly gave her permission, so he stayed on but he also travelled back to Ireland for certain ceremonies which were carried out there.

Now it came about that Ferdiad had returned to Ireland for the great meeting of heroes at the Hall of Tara and amongst the company were Fergus of the short spear and Ferdiad's friend and fellow hero, Cuchullin.

The talk amongst the heroes turned to the subject of the Queen who ruled in Skye and of how she conquered heroes and made them serve in her college of learning for a year and a day. Fergus and some of the other lesser heroes told of their defeat by Sgiath and how they had to serve under her in her college. Fergus especially praised the great skill of Sgiath and spoke of the things he had learnt in her college. Cuchullin, however, laughed at Fergus, telling him he was past his prime and no woman could beat a hero.

Fergus said, 'You are only a young pup yourself. Perhaps it would take a woman to teach you manners.'

Now Ferdiad, for whom Cuchullin had great respect, joined in telling of how Sgiath had overcome him in combat and he not only had served in her college for a year and a day but had also gone back to gain more knowledge and would be back again. 'Perhaps you and I will meet again there,' he said to Cuchullin, 'or can it be that you are afraid to try yourself out against a woman like Sgiath?'

Cuchullin was angered by this reply but could not refuse such a challenge and as soon as the ceremony in the Great Hall of Tara was complete, he sailed off on his journey to the Isle of Skye to challenge and overcome Sgiath.

chapter twenty-eight

hen he arrived in Skye, he landed in the south near what is now Ardvasar and saw no Amazons, nor any extra skilled in arms. Yet he thought, 'They are as my mother who was their kind said – tall strong but quiet in their ways.'

As he roamed in the south, he heard again the rumours of a Queen in the North of Skye who had a bodyguard of women and he decided to travel to the north. After many days, he came to Glendale. When he came to the glen, he saw the beauty of it and it became to him his glen of love, the very land of Tir nan Og which all carry in their heart or in their dreams. For quiet and bonny was the glen with peace lying upon it like a blessing, invisible, but always there.

Coming down the hill into the glen at the flat land called the Gallanach, Cuchullin met a maid, sweet of face and fine of form and in her hand she carried a stout stave. Cuchullin said to the maid, 'You surely drive the cattle hard when you carry a stick so heavy.'

But the maid answered him, 'I carry the stick to teach manners to beardless boys like yourself.'

At that, Cuchullin was put out of face and to redeem his pride, he laughed and said, 'Manners I have and need not even a stick to teach them to a graceless lass,' and went to catch her by the arm. Great was his astonishment when the lass by a quick movement of hand and leg landed him on his back amidst the weeds, which she also pointed out was the right place for him. He sprang to his feet to catch the lass but she evaded him and rapped his ribs with her stick so that his breath caught and, though she was but a lass, he had to use all his strength before eventually he pinned her down.

'Now that I have you in my power,' said he, 'though I admit you left your mark on me with your stick, I would know of you if you are one of Sgiath's maids of war for I have sought for Sgiath for many weary weeks and travelled far to prove she is not equal to a man.'

The girl said she was indeed one of Sgiath's maids of war but said she, 'You will need to be a better man than you've shown me for Sgiath is equal to two of you.' Yet she agreed to take Cuchullin to Sgiath's court, where she trained her Amazons and outfought any man who dared to face her.

The place of Sgiath's court was called the Field of the One man and was in the area now called Hamaraveirin. There still stood there until recent times the upright stones of Sgiath's hall but now even they are gone. At that time, the Great Stones stood in a double circle, the outer ring of which were the dwelling rooms of Sgiath and her Court and in the centre circle was the area where she trained her maids of war and fought against those who dared. The entrance to the centre was formed by four upright stones with great flat stones on top forming a covered way some twelve feet high and broad.

Through this entrance now came Cuchullin and stood in the very centre of the inner circle and spoke so all could hear. 'I challenge Sgiath to combat to prove she is not equal to a man.'

Now Sgiath looked from the window of her chamber to see who challenged her in such a way and saw he was a comely beardless youth and felt a warmth towards him so that she answered, 'I take up your challenge, beardless and nameless one, but we shall fight with the weapons nature gave us and as nature made us and if I overcome you, you will dwell here with me and learn all my arts of arms. If you overcome me, then you shall leave this place in peace and you can boast that you were the one man to overcome Sgiath.'

'So be it,' said Cuchullin and removed his weapons, armour and clothing. Then Sgiath stepped out into the inner circle and Cuchullin saw her for the first time. She was a woman of maturity and in her prime, tall and strongly built, yet graceful and well-formed. Her face was handsome more than pretty and pride and dignity showed in it.

The two of them, having sized each other up, began to wrestle and the watching circle of Amazons shouted in pleasure to see such combat. First it would seem that Cuchullin's strength would overpower Sgiath, then with a cunning thrust or throw she would turn the tide against him so that she gained the upper hand. But yet again, before a decisive throw or hold was made, Cuchullin would gain the advantage.

So it went on for some two hours, yet Cuchullin could not prevail and felt his strength begin to wane. Then he summoned up all his reserves to make one tremendous effort to overcome Sgiath and when he did so, the maids of war saw the hero light shine round his head and knew him for one of the heroes of Ireland. He rushed upon Sgiath and lifted her bodily to slam her down upon the ground. But as he did so, she used his own strength against him so that he was catapulted over her head and crashed against the wall so that the breath was knocked from his body. Before he could recover, Sgiath had the death hold on him so that he had to yield or die.

Yield indeed did Cuchullin and he dwelt with Sgiath at her court and learned from her the arts of war. He was a quick and clever pupil and he even accompanied Sgiath to fight against the heroes who tried to invade Skye and his reputation grew until it was known in all the lands.

chapter twenty-nine

espite Sgiath's forbearance because of the *Geisa*, Aoife was still an annoyance to her and kept disrupting the peace of her lands. Her raids were becoming more numerous and persistent and she was using the protection of the *Geisa*, knowing Sgiath would not breach it by taking up arms and personally killing or seriously injuring her. However, things had reached a stage where some action must be taken.

Now with Cuchullin in her college, Sgiath felt she had the person who could solve her problem. She spoke to him, telling him of her frustration and also telling him how he could solve her dilemma, if he dared to take on such a task.

'I accept both the dare and the task,' replied Cuchullin, for no hero turns his back on a dare. 'I have heard stories of Aoife that claim she is a great warrior second only to yourself. But I will go against her to show that I am the greater warrior and I shall overcome her in the way you have described, for you are the only one, man or women, who has ever beaten me and I would be your one man.'

Having made his vow, Cuchullin waited for the next incursion by Aoife and, when it came, he was ready to meet her with a band of Sgiath's Amazon warriors. Cuchullin had learned from Sgiath that Aoife's most prized possession was her horse, Macha, who led her chariot into battle and killed many men itself. He had also spoken to several other heroes to find out all he could about Aoife. Many of them described Aoife as a great warrior, some even went as far as to compare her with Sgiath, sometimes to the detriment of Sgiath. A few even claimed that Aoife was the greater warrior and they believed this was the reason Sgiath had not faced up to her, rather than the *Geisa* which was upon Sgiath.

The heroes who said this were corrected by Cuchullin and if they persisted in their idea of the might of Aoife, Cuchullin would demonstrate to them, sometimes to their severe injury, just how great he was but always pointing out that Sgiath had beaten him in single combat.

Soon, however, came the day when Aoife made another incursion into the lands of Sgiath and Cuchullin had to meet her army with his band of Amazons. It was a clash of the Titans, with both armies well tried veterans of war and, through the middle of their ranks drove Aoife and Cuchullin in their chariots of war. The ranks of both armies drew apart to allow the chariots of the leaders to meet in combat. The chariots of Cuchullin and Aoife drove on a collision course at great speed with neither wavering nor swinging from their course. But then both chariots came to a halt when only feet apart.

Cuchullin challenged Aoife to meet him in single combat on foot with sword and spear. Whoever was the victor would claim all the spoils. If Aoife won, she would get the lands of Sgiath and become Queen of Skye, but if Cuchullin won, Aoife would have to swear never to take up arms or plot against Sgiath and she must go and live in a faraway land, never returning to Eilean Sgia – the land of shadows – or the misty isle. Both having sworn to abide by the terms, combat began and both armies watched in awe.

The two combatants sprang from their chariots with swords in hand and spear shining on their backs. The swords they used were the great two-handed claymores which, in the hands of a skilled swordsman, could shear through the bodies of three men in a single stroke, yet in their skilled hands could parry and fend off most attacks of another swordsman. No shields were used. Success or failure depended on your skill and ability and now here were two acknowledged masters of the swords putting all their skills to the ultimate test.

Cuchullin went in with a full blooded swing, hoping to catch Aoife by surprise but she leapt high in the air so that Cuchullin's blade passed below her feet and, whilst she was still in mid-air, launched a downward cut at Cuchullin's head.

Cuchullin leapt to his left and made a backhand swing at Aoife but she parried it and the swords clashed and rang with sparks flying from their edges as they rasped together. The blows and lunges flowed from both combatants and each felt the strength of wrist and arm of the other. Neither could gain a decisive advantage and the combat went on without pause for over an hour. Then Aoife launched yet another cross cut swing of the sword, which Cuchullin parried with an upright blade but, as the swords met, Cuchullin's blade shattered, leaving him with only the hilt. Aoife was ready to deliver the death blow when Cuchullin cried out, 'Macha has gone down!'

Aoife glanced quickly towards her horse and, in that moment, Cuchullin seized her by the breasts and lifted her above his head. The sword fell from Aoife's fingers as she was lifted and Cuchullin held her there, feeling as he did the strength drain from her body. When the last of her strength was gone and she was limp in his grasp, Cuchullin carried her to his tent and there he entered her with his horn of manhood and they became lovers.

So Cuchullin conquered Aoife in the way that Sgiath had told him yet his one love was Sgiath. Aoife had to fulfil the promise she had made to Cuchullin and leave him and the land of Alba, yet she said to him, 'You are the love of my heart and your seed is in me, yet you will never know the son I bear you and you shall kill your other son whom you also will never know.'

After saying this, she left Cuchullin and Alba and Cuchullin returned to his one true love, Sgiath.

chapteR thiRty

he defeat and banishment of Aoife
brought peace to the lands of
Sgiath and she used this peace to
promote and extend her college of
learning so that it became famous,
not only in Alba but in all the world.
Students now came to Skye from every country
and all who were willing to learn were welcome.
Every country in Europe, especially Ireland, had
their students in the college of Sgiath and many
others from distant countries such as Persia, Egypt,
China and India also had students at the college. It
was hailed as the greatest college in all the world. It
was so successful that, whilst Lomharsgil remained
the hub, other colleges were set up in places such
as Uist, Iona (I Druidhran), Hirta, Arran and even
eventually in other countries such as France, Spain,
Germany and even China.

The colleges taught the Druidical knowledge
but it was not written down, though the Druids
had the ability to read and write. They believed
that use of memory made the intake and
preservation of knowledge far superior to that of
the written word, so their precepts of medicine,
science and other arts were taught mainly in the

open and in such a way that the retention in memory was complete.

One of the methods employed was the Cearcall Lom (the naked circle). In this, the tutor and the scholars sat naked in a circle, with the tutor at the East. Each person would have their knees touching the next person on each side and would have their hand on the shoulders of the persons next to them. The tutor would tell a story or a poem or tell a recipe for making medicine from different plants. Starting with the person on the left of the tutor, each scholar in turn would recite what had been said and by the time it came back to the tutor everyone in the circle knew the thing they had to learn. The number in the circle was usually quite small – often about 12 – but was always bound by the rule of three. For example, the greatest number taught at one time was 81 but this was split into nine groups of nine.

Students who wished to become healers had a very severe discipline imposed on them and only the best were allowed to continue for the full extent of the course, for example, after a time of learning in various herbs and vital foods. They would be sent naked into the moors and hills to survive for a month and learn the ways of nature and the voices of the plants, water, wind and that of the insects, especially the wisdom of the bees. If they were successful in this, they were trained on for ten years before being allowed to go out on their own as healers. The final arbiter on their ability was Donran, the greatest healer of all.

Sgiath oversaw every discipline but always gave precedence to the tutors who worked with the students on the ground and her colleges or universities were also renowned for their fairness to rich and poor pupils alike.

One day a man came to Lomharsgil and presented himself to Sgiath. He was a tall, well-built man with the red-gold hair and blue eyes of the Celts. He told Sgiath that he had travelled to many lands in search of knowledge but then he had heard reports of her colleges of teaching and spoken to some who had studied at them. Now he himself wished to be accepted as a pupil to learn from the best and then to go to a land he knew to bring to the people there the wisdom of the Druids and their great knowledge of nature, science and art.

Sgiath was impressed by the man and his sincerity but said to him, 'We teach all equally here but to enter our places of teaching, each applicant must face a test, usually one of combat. However, we do have other criterion by which we judge the suitability of an applicant. In your case, we have today a race to the top of Sealbh Mhor. The winner is the one who reaches the top first and brings down the wooden cuach (Quaich) which is at the centre of the top of the hill but on the way down they must fill it at the waterfall of knowledge and bring it here to me without spilling a drop. All the runners in the race run naked as nature made us so that no advantage can be gained or lost. If you are willing to run in this race, tired as you are from travelling, then we will judge on your deeds if you are worthy of a place at our college.'

'If that is the task you put on me, I shall do my best to fulfil it,' he replied and went to join the other runners, leaving his clothing at the starting place called the Gallanach.

When the race was started by a signal from Sgiath, he ran in a group behind the leaders but soon found out that many of the competition were more than willing to use their elbows and shoulders to stagger other runners and gain slight advantage. However, he had run in such races before and avoided being involved in such minor tussles.

As they approached the summit of Sealbh Mhor, a group of three runners broke away from the leading group and he sprinted to catch up with them. By this time, several of the original starters had dropped out of the race. He, however, maintained his burst of speed and caught up with the three leaders. As the group came on to the level sward of the top of the mountain, one man burst away from the group and sprinted to the wooden cuach, lifting it in triumph before turning and running back down the mountain slope to the waterfall of knowledge, where he filled the cuach and placed his left hand over the top of it to prevent it spilling, yet even as he did so he was jostled by two of the runners who had reached the summit with him. Seeing this, the stranger in the race interposed and pushed the other two away from the carrier of the cuach and continued to support and protect him on the run back to Sgiath, though he was greatly disappointed that he had failed to win.

When they arrived back at the Gallanach, Sgiath congratulated the winner and gave to him the title of Luran, which he would bear and be honoured for the next year. Then she turned to the stranger and said to him, 'You ran well though you did not win but you showed your worth by treating fairly the one who did. You are welcome as a pupil at my college but now we must know your name so that you will no longer be a stranger.'

'Gladly shall I join your college,' he replied, 'and I shall be delighted to learn at your feet all the knowledge of every kind that I can absorb. My name is Ramas.'

Ramas stayed in the college of Sgiath for five years and in that time he became a favourite pupil of all the teachers, for as they said he was so willing to learn and soaked up knowledge like spagnum moss soaks up water or blood.

At the end of five years, Ramas came to Sgiath to tell her he was leaving the college to travel and make his own destiny. Sgiath was sorry to see him go but she and the Old Grey Magician agreed that the time was right for him to leave, as he had absorbed their knowledge and wisdom and would gather more in his travels.

The Old Grey Magician said to Ramas, 'The day will come when you will be the leader of a great nation and your name will be remembered when ours are forgotten.'

Ramas sailed away from the same bay he had landed at and in memory of him it was called Ramasaig (the Bay of Ramas) and with him went three or four of the tutors in the college of Sgiath who wanted to face the challenge of new lands.

chapter thirty-one

n the golden times, when Sgiath and Cuchullin held sway and in their hands justice was equal for all, there came to Sgiath's court a man asking for justice for himself and for his clan.

Sgiath said to the man, 'Before we can mete out justice, we must know how you have been wronged, if indeed wrong there be. So tell your tale to us in council here and we shall decide if truth be in it and what action should be taken.'

So he began to tell his tale – the Saga of the Fairy Cattle – which is still told where people tell of the deeds of the heroes.

It came about that Aoidh, for so was named the man, had met and fallen in love with a red-haired maiden, not knowing that she was one of the Sluagh (or fairy Host). Though even knowing that might have made no difference.

As happens often when such a love occurs, there came the day when his fairy wife had to leave him to return to her own land, though she was sad to do so. As a last gift to her husband, she gave to him a milk white cow, saying to him that so long as the cow was on his land no one in the land would thirst for milk and the finest of calves would be his.

What she had told Aoidh was true indeed and his possessions and those of his clan increased greatly over the years and happiness was theirs. Yet happiness is a hard thing to possess and can lead to envy in those around and so it befell in this case.

The fame of the cow spread to ears that heard with jealous greed and plotted to gain the beast for their own use. Yet this was difficult, as the fairy wife had said that the cow was only held under a spell whilst it was on her husband's land, so taking it by force or by stealing it would serve no purpose.

So the neighbour came to Aoidh under the guise of friendship. He came to the house with gifts and flattering comments on Aoidh's husbandry and management of his cattle and crops. Aoidh made the man welcome in this house and organised a ceilidh for him, with food and drink of the best. The greatest storytelling, fine music of the harp and the sweetest of singers.

Colla invited Aoidh to his own land, feasted him and put on for him a fine ceilidh and spoke fair words to him so that Aoidh believed his friendship to be true. Having won Aoidh's trust, Colla then started the next part of his plan by showing to him his black bull. A fine bull he was, with shining black, shaggy hair and sharp white horns which a man could just span with widespread arms.

Colla said to Aoidh that this bull was also from a
Fairy herd and it had been prophesied that if a day
came when he was mated with a white cow of the
Fairy herd, the progeny of the pair would start a
herd which would be famous and make riches and
happiness for any clan that possessed them.

Aoidh, however, was not interested in Colla's
suggestions for as he said his clan had all the milk
from the white cow that they could need and from
her also they got calves which gave them meat, so
happiness was already theirs. But Colla had a way
of putting things that even a man content with his
lot was made to want more and instead of need
came greed. Colla said to Aoidh that it was also
prophesised that the mating of the two would
bring forth at the first four calves, two bulls and
two heifers, each of the bulls black and each of the
heifers white. The second mating would bring forth
four red heifers and from then on, the mating of
the progeny would bring a mixing of these colours
but always the race would be known against all
others by their horns the span of a man's arms. The
progeny of the first and second matings, said Colla,
would be divided between their two clans so both
would be blessed with plenty and live in harmony.

Still Aoidh was not persuaded but said to Colla
that the cow could not be taken from his land.
Colla had an answer ready which seemed a fair
solution. He said to Aoidh, 'I will be prepared to

bring my bull to your land and, while the matings take place, my men and I will stay at the top of your glen and once the matings are done, we will take our half of the cattle and leave and the land will remain yours with your half of the cattle.'

Now Aoidh was tempted, for his cow, though it gave him calves, they were always bull calves so he could not carry on the breed. Yet until Colla planted the seed in his mind he had been happy to accept things as they were.

He accepted Colla's words and allowed him to bring his bull and his men to his land and to mate the black bull with his fine white cow. Just as Colla had said, the matings produced the eight calves and Aoidh asked for the division to be made and for Colla and his men to return to his own land.

Colla laughed in his face for he now had the cow, the bull and also the calves and he had also a hero from a far island, a man called Ascall, tall as a tree who slew men like corn. Colla had it all, nor would he part with any and when Aoidh with some of his clan tried to get what was rightfully theirs, Ascall and Colla's men killed most of them.

Now Aoidh stood in Sgiath's court and pled for justice. Sgiath admitted that he had been wronged and it was done within her boundaries so must be put right by her. She would take some of her Amazons and go to right the wrong that had been done.

Then spoke Cuchullin. 'I have listened to this man and I ask that this task be put upon me, for I know of this Ascall and of his deeds and I would try my metal against his.'

'The task is yours and I wish you well in it but you shall take with you seven of my Amazons that your back may not be bare,' replied Sgiath

So Cuchullin went to the land of Aoidh and, with him, the seven Amazons and Aoidh himself.

When they all arrived in the land of Aoidh, Cuchullin sent him to a knoll to speak to Colla. He told Aoidh to shout to Colla that a man with seven women had come to dispense justice and unless Colla agreed to stand by his word to Aoidh, he and his hired hand Ascall would bring death upon their own heads.

Colla heard this message from Aoidh and came to look on this bold hero. But when he saw Cuchullin was but a beardless youth, he laughed and said that neither he nor Ascall need bother themselves, for eight of his clan would brush away the rubbish from their door.

Out to the knoll came eight of his clan but against Cuchullin and the Amazons, they had no chance. One was left alive to carry back to Colla the message that the rubbish needed a stronger brush than he possessed.

Then came Ascall to smite those upstarts and Cuchullin went to meet him in single combat as was the tradition of the heroes. All that day they fought and Ascall knew his end was near for, though he had not wounded Cuchullin, he himself was wounded in many places. So he made a secret sign and out rushed the clan of Colla to attack Cuchullin from behind and that could have been the end for him but the seven Amazons sprang to defend his back and defeated Colla's clan. Cuchullin was enraged by such treachery and hurled Gae-Bolg – his spear which never missed – at Ascall and slew him.

In rage, Colla sent out his bull to kill Cuchullin and it went mad tossing into the air and killing not only some of the Amazons but also many of Colla's clan until it reached Cuchullin. It charged at him but he gripped it by the horns and, with one mighty heave, threw it over his back, breaking its neck and bursting its heart. The very earth shuddered with the force of its fall.

Then Cuchullin took his sword to smite Colla but suddenly a spell came upon them all so that none could move. There appeared the Fairy wife of Aoidh and she spoke to them, saying that the killing must cease. She had done wrong in giving her husband the cow and her husband had been wrong in being tempted by Colla.

Yet had all those things a purpose. Now Colla would be banished to another island and his name and fame would live on in the name of this place and of the island. Aoidh's clan would keep the cattle from the matings of the black bull and the white cow and would remain on their land. Cuchullin would win repute and do many more great deeds and die a hero and his memory would carry on through all the years to come.

'Still,' said she to Aoidh, 'you are all my heart and yet you were not content with what I gave. Your cattle will be famous but you will be forgotten and I too will die. I have returned to live with you and have lost my immortality. Yet I am happy.'

Then she gave to Cuchullin a round shield which had a spell upon it that so long as he held it, he would not be wounded. For she said, 'you have defended the weak and now the weak will defend you, though if you forsake the way of justice and break your *Geisa*, you will lose the shield.'

This was a blessing to Sgiath for Cuchullin got also one of the black bulls of the fairy cow and it was taken to bhaterstein to the place called Aonadh nan Tarbh and from it was bred the black cattle of Glendale with horns the span of a man's arms.

All was not well in Ireland and Cuchullin's own land of Ulster was placed under a magic spell so that the heroes could not defend it and word came to Cuchullin that his people needed him. Cuchullin was sad to go but a promise was on him that he must keep so he bade goodbye to Sgiath. Once again, they met in combat but now Sgiath was no match for Cuchullin for he not only knew all her arts of war but had learned to invent others.

Then Sgiath said, 'You are the man for whom this place is named, for you are the one man who has beaten me and the one man I have loved. Your seed is in me, but you will not know the son I shall bear you. You will return to Skye when the time is right and you will stay here and be slain but my court and I will be no more. I give you now my spear Gae-Bolg which never misses and the magic runes which will bring you safe back to Skye.'
So Cuchullin left Skye for a second time and great became his fame thereafter.

Now with her lands settled and peace in the area, Sgiath could concentrate on her colleges and universities of learning. Her hub of learning remained at Lomharsgil but branch places of teaching were established in other areas and even in other countries but usually each of them specialised in one discipline. For example, the college on the Isle of Arran was a college of surgery and medicine; in it, operations such as trepanning the skull, repairing the brain and re-fixing severed limbs were carried out and the use of herbs as anaesthetic and antiseptics were studied until fully understood. A tutor from the hub would come to these branch colleges to check that the correct procedures were being followed. So to the colleges of medicine came Donran the healer; to the colleges of magic came the Old Grey Magician. Each of the head tutors in Bardic lore, music, art, mathematics and philosophy would also visit the branch colleges and test the pupils and teachers in their own subjects.

Sgiath also set up stones of justice across her kingdoms, where people who had committed crimes would be tried and punished according to laws set down by her. People could also attend the stones of justice if they had been wronged and, if this was proven, then commensurate reparation would be carried out. Sgiath's laws were equal for all whether of high or lowly status.

The laws made by Sgiath and the high standards of teaching set in her colleges, especially in her central college at Lomharsgil, became known in every country in the world. Yet again, Sgiath was to learn that her renown bred envy in those of lesser intellect and skill and this envy soon turned to greed. Sgiath saw this rise against her gathering strength and knew that before long, it would turn to active resentment and she must ready herself to once again defend Skye against invaders.

However, she found this to be no easy task, for her original Amazons were getting on in years and the younger generations had known peace for some time and were no longer willing to fight for they had grown soft mentally and physically. The majority of the people on Skye wanted to compromise with the prospective invaders but Sgiath told them that the invaders' idea of compromise was for their own principles and laws to take the place of those set out by Sgiath. Compromise was only possible if Sgiath and her people gave up everything they had fought for, everything they had taught, their laws of equality and justice for all and their schooling for all classes of people. Sgiath and all her people would have to subject themselves to be governed by countries that hated the teachings and laws of the Druids and would do everything in their powers to wipe out those laws and teachings.

chapter thirty-two

y insisting on the urgency of this danger to her people, Sgiath was able for some time to drive off the attempted invasion of her land by several different Kings from various lands but some of the battles were severe and all of them cost Sgiath more of her forces so that she was forced to fight with fewer and fewer followers.

There came a day when a King from the north landed near Armadale in the south of Skye and started to march northwards. Sgiath knew she was greatly outnumbered but decided to allow him to march his army to near Sligachan, while all the time along his way she led and launched small guerrilla attacks on his forces so that he lost some men and the rest of his army were afraid to sleep in case they were attacked. As his army entered one of the narrow valleys between the mountain and the sea, Sgiath suddenly launched all her followers upon them from the mountainside so that the King's army was trapped between her army and the sea.

Sgiath was at the head of the famed triangle formed by her army and she drove into the very heart of the opposing army of the northern King, killing all in her path until she reached the King himself. He was a great warrior in his own right and faced Sgiath with his great axe, wielding it with great dexterity.

As they battled, Sgiath's followers protected Sgiath's back and made sure that none of the King's men would attack her from behind. The combat between Sgiath and the King was fierce and furious. Both of them were warriors of note, well skilled in the use of their weapons, but the King was young and aware that Sgiath was no longer a young woman, so he fought with maximum speed to force Sgiath to respond rapidly. He felt that she would tire under his fierce attack giving him an opening to kill her. After some time, he himself began to tire and, as he did so, Sgiath escalated the fury of her own attack. The King realised that he was going to be defeated and made a sign to bring his men to attack Sgiath but her few remaining Amazons had formed a circle around the King and Sgiath, so his tired men were not able to break the circle. Sgiath attacked even more ferociously and, with a slash below the King's shield, she brought him to his knees.

The King realised his time had come and pleaded for his life but, with the bloodthirst of battle in her and her need to send a message to others likely to invade, she paid him no heed. As he knelt before her, with one sweep of her

sword, she cut off his head then picked it up and
waved it above her head for all his army to see.
His men, having lost their leader, gave up the fight.
Sgiath was merciful to them and let them live,
knowing they would carry to others the story of
their defeat and the decapitation of their King by
Sgiath. She believed this might cause others to think
again before they invaded the land of Sgiath or her
colleges of education.

Sgiath and the remains of her army returned in
triumph but she knew that, in time, other envious
tribes would invade and she no longer had her
Amazon warriors in sufficient numbers to resist all
attacks. Until she no longer had any followers, she
would fight to protect her land and colleges which
were now her great pleasure in life.

Although Sgiath now concentrated upon the
teachings in her colleges and ensured that the very
best tutors were used in every discipline, there
were several arts that could not be taught but
appeared as gifts bestowed on certain people that
could not be passed to others. The first follower
of Sgiath, Enya, possessed the gift of 'Suen' and
Sgiath remembered well the time Enya had used
it to save her little band of five – Sgiath herself,
Enya and three others. They were being hunted by
a large company of armed men thirsty for revenge
and they were trapped in a narrow glen with no
escape. Sgiath decided they could all die bravely by
turning and launching an attack upon their enemies

as there was no cover sufficient to conceal them. Enya, however, said to them to stand still about ten feet off the track until their enemies went past. They did as Enya said and, to their amazement, all of their enemies went past without seeing them.

'How on earth did that happen?' Sgiath asked Enya.

Enya replied, 'It is called Suen. I have had the ability since I was a child. If you wish, I can try to pass it to you.'

Sgiath was delighted to try but, to both their disappointments, they discovered Enya could not pass it to Sgiath. After Enya died, Sgiath tried to find others with the gift who could pass it on but discovered that very few people had this ability. It appeared to be carried in certain families but even in those families it was only given to one person and could skip generations.

Another gift which could not be passed on was that of Second Sight. It could be passed on by physical contact but only on a temporary basis, sometimes only lasting for one vision while physical contact was maintained. At its very best, the passing on lasted for the lifetime of the person but, even then, it was not passed on to that person's family. ESP and telekinesis could be learned in her colleges, though it was noted that people taught to use these were never quite up to the high standard of those in whom the senses were inherent.

As it came about, Sgiath was not given much time to enjoy the peace she had brought to her lands for all too soon after her battle against the northern King, the 'Small Dark Men' began to invade. This invasion was different to those before, with many determined forces coming to attack. If they were beaten in battle, they withdrew for a time, re-enforced their army and attacked again. They were good, well-trained fighters and soon Sgiath was aware that her army had been reduced to a handful. She could no longer defend the island unaided.

In her desperation, she sent her son who was also the son of Cuchullin to Ireland to find his father and give him the message that Sgiath wished him to come back to Skye to defend it against the Small Dark Men. She put a *Geisa* on their son that when he went to Ireland, he would give his name to no one and would never refuse to fight a hero. The son, who was a hero in his own right and had been well trained by Sgiath, agreed to the *Geisa* she put upon him, though she told him neither he nor Cuchullin would ever see her when they came back to Skye.

So their son went to Ireland, where he fought other heroes and met his father. Cuchullin came back to Skye to defend it against the Small Dark Men but the deeds of the son and his father are stories to be told at another time.

Bibliography

MANY OF THE BOOKS consulted served only to
confirm and roughly date some of the oral stories
as the subjects taught in the Druidical colleges.
References in these books, parchments and
manuscripts are usually very short with little detail.
Several of them refer to Gaelic and Irish heroes
travelling to Skye (The Isle of Shadows), including
Cuchullin, for their final tuition in science, art and
war but give no details of that training or how the
colleges were set up.

I also looked into modern books on the
Celtic Druids but discovered that most of them
reiterated what had been said by previous writers
and in general did not appear to bring much new
information about or understanding of the life or
ways of Sgiath or her colleges.

While I have studied many books and old
manuscripts I have not used direct quotes from them
in this book but have used them to corroborate
some of the stories. In the case of some early Roman
historians, I have used my own translation of the Latin
text and in early Gaelic writings, I have depended on a
friend who was a very knowledgeable Gaelic scholar.

Many of the references to Celtic Druidism
are based on Caesar's *De Bello Gallico* which
shows the respect the Romans had for the
teachings of the Druids and the colleges run by
them. Unfortunately, it does not define where

these colleges were but does give some idea of the subjects taught. The Romans, however, did their utmost to eradicate Druidism and, as part of this, set up their own colleges where youth could be taught in circa 61 AD. One big difference in these Roman colleges was that writing was employed as a teaching standard and was only available to the wealthy whilst in the Druidic colleges started by Sgiath, oral teaching was the main standard as they believed this gave greater power to the memory and surpassed written knowledge even though they, as is noted by Caesar, Tacitus, Pliny and other Roman historians, had the ability to both read and write.

It must be remembered that some of the writers mentioned above based some of their work on that of Suetonius and Posidonius of the 1st century BC and later works are very much biased to display the superiority of Roman teachings and the ways of the Celtic Druids were derided. To render them abhorrent to others, great stories were told of the sacrifices of hundreds of human beings at various ritual sites but no proof of these hundreds of mass killings has been found.

Yet even the Romans writing as enemies of the Druids concede that their colleges of learning taught thousands of pupils from all over the world, of all classes. Even in the ancient Sanskrit Indian writing of about 1500 BC, references are made to the great renowned centres of learning in the British Isles and the Vedic 'rui' and 'vid' can be combined to mean 'Masters of Knowledge'.

Victorian historians were very much against any approval of the Druidic system although, by their time, the Roman civilisation and the Christian Churches – especially the Roman Catholic Church – had greatly diluted the Druidic system, by condemning their teachings and, where rituals and ceremonies were too popular to be overcome, by incorporating them and many of the Druidical Saints into the rites of the Christian churches. For example, Brighid became St Bride and Oestre became Easter. However, despite this, Druidism has been preserved to a large extent in the oral tradition of many countries, especially Scotland.

SOURCES

Historians
Donald Monro, 'Dean of the Isles', 1549
Martin Martin, 1695
Pliny, *c.*1 ad
Pomponius Mela *c.*1 ad
Professor Magnus Maclean FRSE MIEE MICE LLD
 (1857–1937)
Ptolemy of Alexandria, 120 ad
Timogenes, Diodorus, Dio Chrysostom and
 Alexandrious

Books
Táin Bó Cúailnge (The Raiding of the Cattle
 of Cooley)
Various, *The Annals of the Kingdom of Ireland*, 1848

Julius Caesar, *De Bello Gallico*, 55 BC

Keltie et al. *A history of the Scottish Highlands, Highland clans and Highland regiments*, 1793

Charles Squire, *Celtic myth & legend, poetry & romance*, 1912

TW Rolleston, *Celtic Myths and Legends*, 1911

Alexander Nicolson (ed.), *Gaelic Proverbs*, 1881

Alexander Nicolson, *History of Skye*, 1930

Sanskrit Manuscript, *c.*1500 BC

Dr JF Anderson, *Proceedings of the Society of Antiquaries of Scotland*, 2003

Bibracte (Enamels)

Caitlin Matthews & John Matthews, *The Encyclopaedia of Celtic Wisdom: The Celtic Shaman's Sourcebook*, 1994

Bob Curran, *Complete Guide to Celtic Mythology*, 2000

Michael Baigent and Richard Leigh, *The Dead Sea Scrolls Deception*, 1991

Godfrey Higgins, *The Celtic Druids*, 1827

Michael Tsarion, *The Irish Origins of Civilization, Volume One: The Servants of Truth: Druidic Traditions & Influence Explored*, 2012

EA Wallis Budge, *The Book of the Dead*, 2008

Lorraine MacDonald & Sam McSkimming, *Gods of the Celts*, 1992

George W Macpherson, *Highland Myths and Legends*, 2001

George W Macpherson, *The Old Grey Magician*, 2016

vocabulary

Suen (Gaelic)
The ability not to be seen (not Invisibility);
    an enchantment or spell

Sgiath (Gaelic); Scáthach, Sgathaich (Irish)
Shadowy; winged; shield; target. Also printed as
    Scia on old documents and maps

Ach nan Aon Duine (Gaelic)
Field of the one man. Place where Cuchullin and
    Sgiath first met and fought

Gallanach (Gaelic)
Place of the young saplings or young men or place
    of the stranger

Earrasaid (Gaelic)
Female form of phillimore, formed from piece of
    tartan cloth 8 by 1.5 yards held by belt at waist

Gae-Bolg (Gaelic)
A special spear, sometimes multi-barbed
    and poisoned

Gleann na gall (Gaelic)
Glen of the stranger

Lomharsgil (Gaelic)
Place of the magic or shining art

Tir nan Og (Gaelic)
Land of the ever young

Magistre Sapientiae (Latin)
Master of all knowledge

Mordhu or Mordha (Gaelic)
Name of Wise Woman, meaning great or excellent

Ard Ban Righ (Gaelic)
High Queen

Ard Righ (Gaelic)
High King

Seannachaidh (Gaelic)
High grade storyteller and bard

Claidheamh Luinn (Gaelic)
Sword of light

Macarluinn (Gaelic)
Son of light (sword of Fionn)

Coivi
Druid or Druidical priest

Fir Beag Dorcha (Gaelic)
Small Dark Men

notes

1. One of the mysteries about Sgiath is what appears to be the inexplicable stretch of her lifetime, far beyond what is now accepted as a standard life span. This, however, may be a no longer acceptable fact that the ancients may actually have had much longer lives than we have at present. If we look in the Bible, we can find several examples of people living to be hundreds of years old, for example, Methuselah. If we study some of the writings on early Celtic lives, we discover very extreme ages attributed to several people, such as Ossian, Caoilte, Eithne, Juan and Fintan, some of whom exceeded even Methuselah in age.

2. Whilst every effort has been made to keep this book as close to the original oral story as possible, some licence has been used to link the stories using my knowledge of the oral tradition, and a combination of oral tradition and written records has been used to give some chronological order to Sgiath's life. By doing this, it is hoped to give a foundation for future research, for there is much more of her life which may be preserved in other oral traditions and in other ancient books and manuscripts which I did not have access to. Much ancient knowledge has been rediscovered in recent

years and, in the present time, who knows what is still hidden, not only in Scotland but in other countries all round the world?

3. When the tomb of Ramesses was found and his mummy was opened, it was discovered that he had yellow hair which had been red gold when he was younger. His features had been the aquiline Celtic caucasian type. In some very old Gaelic documents, Ramasaig is spelt Ramisaig or Ramesaidh.

4. Several modern writers such as Lorraine MacDonald and Sam MacSkimming in their book, *Gods of the Celts*, give Sgiath the place of a Goddess in the panoply of Celtic Gods and Goddesses. Some of the older writers imply this without stating it as a fact. Perhaps one of the reasons for this is that Sgiath seems to just disappear. As for all I could find out, there are no stories of her death or burial place that can usually be found of heroes. Is it perhaps possible that she is the third unnamed hero who is said to lie in a cavern below a hill in Skye, meant to come alive and save Scotland when its need is greatest. The other two are named as Fionn and Ossian and, in the case of Ossian, there are no definite stories of his death or place of burial, though many theories have been explored for both.

Many of the heroes of both Scotland and Ireland are claimed to have had huge life spans.

Ossian is said to have lived to over 300 years and, if the diaries of St Patrick as recorded by the monks are to be believed, this should be true as the conversations of Patrick and Ossian could only have taken place if he lived over 300 years. In Ireland, Caoilte, grandson of Fionn MacCumhail, fought in battle of Ollarba (Annals of the Four Masters) circa 285 and lived on to meet St Patrick. Eithne lived several hundred years and also met St Patrick. Could such longevity explain some of the apparent overlaps of timescale between various episodes in the life of Sgiath?

5. Most modern researchers concur with the idea that the Cuchullin Cycle pertains to Ireland, whilst the Sgiath and Fionn stories are Scottish but were carried to Ireland and preserved there although being given a fresh, Christian slant. Fir Beag Dorcha (Small Dark Men) are mentioned in both Scottish and Irish stories, but it is unexplained who they were or where they came from, though some attempts have been made to link them with the Firbolg.

6. It is worthy of note that the Ainu people of Japan and the Maori people of New Zealand both have legends descended from Celts and both have red-haired blue-eyed people in their number. The Maori also claim that their tattoos are based on ancient Celtic designs, as are some of the weapons of both tribes.

7. The sword that Sgiath took from the cannibal chief is later mentioned with the appellation, 'sword of light'. This appears to bring it into line with other famous swords: 'the sword of the son of light', for example, is chosen by Fionn and Excalibur is connected to Arthur. In each case, the recipient of the sword has to perform a task and thereafter the sword has magical powers. None of the swords are preserved now but it is known that the Druidical smiths made steel over 3,000 years ago.

Luath Press Limited

committed to publishing well written books worth reading

LUATH PRESS takes its name from Robert Burns, whose little collie Luath (*Gael.*, swift or nimble) tripped up Jean Armour at a wedding and gave him the chance to speak to the woman who was to be his wife and the abiding love of his life. Burns called one of the 'Twa Dogs' Luath after Cuchullin's hunting dog in Ossian's *Fingal*. Luath Press was established in 1981 in the heart of Burns country, and is now based a few steps up the road from Burns' first lodgings on Edinburgh's Royal Mile. Luath offers you distinctive writing with a hint of unexpected pleasures.

Most bookshops in the UK, the US, Canada, Australia, New Zealand and parts of Europe, either carry our books in stock or can order them for you. To order direct from us, please send a £sterling cheque, postal order, international money order or your credit card details (number, address of cardholder and expiry date) to us at the address below. Please add post and packing as follows: UK – £1.00 per delivery address; overseas surface mail – £2.50 per delivery address; overseas airmail – £3.50 for the first book to each delivery address, plus £1.00 for each additional book by airmail to the same address. If your order is a gift, we will happily enclose your card or message at no extra charge.

Luath Press Limited
543/2 Castlehill
The Royal Mile
Edinburgh EH1 2ND
Scotland
Telephone: +44 (0)131 225 4326 (24 hours)
email: sales@luath. co.uk
Website: www. luath.co.uk